CALL

CW00696887

CALLED TO CARE?

A handbook for Christians considering
nursing as a career

Mary Endersbee

HODDER AND STOUGHTON
LONDON SYDNEY AUCKLAND TORONTO

British Library Cataloguing in Publication Data

Endersbee, Mary
  Called to care?
  1. Medicine. Nursing – Christian viewpoints
  I. Title
  261.561

  ISBN 0-340-51743-3

Contents

Preface

by Baroness Caroline Cox
RGN, BSC, MSC (Econ.), FRCN

Are you thinking of becoming a nurse? And are you a Christian (or perhaps trying to be one, often rather unsatisfactorily, like me)? Then you might be interested to know I never regretted having become a nurse.

First, nursing, by its very nature, gives us opportunities to respond to Christ's invitation to care for our fellow human beings. Indeed, He told us that if we give a glass of water to someone in His name, we are giving it to Him – what an awesome privilege!

Secondly, nursing is a form of companionship which allows us to walk with others as they pass through experiences of illness, injury, infirmity and, finally, the valley of the shadow of death. This is one reason why nursing has been called 'the major caring profession'. Only nurses stay with patients and their loved ones, providing intimate care around the clock. This privilege often provides opportunities to comfort and to console which are not so readily available to other professions. Many a nurse on night duty finds that a patient awake in the small hours of the morning is grateful to be able to confide in him or her, talking about fears and anxieties in ways which are impossible in the hurly-burly of the day, or in a busy clinic.

Thirdly, nursing provides a magnificent variety of different kinds of service – in hospital, in the community, in this country or abroad. You literally have the world at your feet. You may choose to work in an inner city area of an industrial society; or you may wish to use your qualification to serve Christ in the mission field in a developing country. There is always a need for health workers and an opportunity to offer a Christian witness of Love in Action. And there is also a splendid variety of different kinds of nursing, ranging from health education and disease prevention to care of the mentally or physically ill and handicapped.

You can also choose between different kinds of specialist nursing. For example, you might prefer to specialise in caring for the very young in Special Care Baby Units, with a particular ministry not only to the infants but also to their anxious parents; or you could choose to care for children. Alternatively, you might find great satisfaction in looking after adults in high dependency care, as in Intensive or Coronary Care Units. Conversely, your 'calling' might be to care for the infirm elderly either in residential care or in their own homes.

So there is a wonderful range of different opportunities – all valuable, valued forms of service. But be warned! Nursing cannot, must not, be an easy job. If undertaken in a spirit of love, it will require compassion. The literal meaning of that word is to 'suffer with'. I am sure you never thought that nursing would be a soft option. But the strains and pressures can come in unexpected ways, especially when you are tired and stressed. So may I humbly offer a word of advice? If, after having thought and prayed about your decision, you believe God is calling you into nursing, then go forward in faith; when difficult days come as they almost certainly will, remember that you made the decision in good faith; and that God will use your willingness to serve Him through serving His people, in ways which may be past understanding. But, whatever happens, He is a faithful God and He will enable you having done all, to stand.

May I finish by saying that, if you do decide nursing is for you, I hope you will find it full of rich rewards. I am not talking about salaries! I am talking about the infinitely precious rewards which come with the immense privilege of helping others in need, and of the joy of giving an ultimately worthwhile service.

Baroness Caroline Cox
26 March 1990

Foreword

by Dame Audrey Emerton,
Chairwoman of the United Kingdom Central Council

Choosing a career is not always easy, especially with so many career opportunities competing in the market place. How do you know you are making the right choice? This is a very important question to anyone setting out on a career path but particularly for the Christian.

Nursing is described as the major caring profession and within the profession there are many specialities to choose to work in.

As one looks back into the history of nursing it is clear that nursing care was based in the religious orders. Today most nursing care is delivered in a secular setting either in a hospital or in the home, but still requires an holistic approach; that is care of the body, mind and spirit of the individual.

Nursing in the past has been regarded as a job which requires 'soothing of the fevered brow' or offering 'tender, loving care'. Both remain important, but nursing is a profession which has developed over the years, and now requires knowledge in biological and social sciences and skills in the practice of nursing, some of which call for a knowledge of high technology, as well as good inter-personal skills.

A nurse is placed in a most privileged position being closest to people in their greatest need, either caring for the patient who is very sick, in severe pain or dying, or for the relatives of a very sick or dying patient.

A midwife on the other hand shares in the joy of a new life when delivering babies.

Following qualification 'the world' is your oyster and the opportunities for practising nursing skills either at home or abroad are enormous. At home, the National Health Service provides opportunities for developing further the skills acquired in Pre-Registration training, allowing for specialisation in all areas of nursing care. In addition, there is opportunity to work in the private sector, industry, local authority or the armed services, to name a few.

Many nurses wish to travel and the scope for this is enormous, and for the Christian nurse the call to missionary work provides many openings in a vast number of countries. Thus many nurses have, in the past, served the Lord in mission hospitals or clinics through the auspices of missionary societies. There is no doubt that there is a mission field for the Christian nurse either at home or abroad.

But the path is not always an easy one – especially when friends are at university enjoying long holidays and weekends free; working unsocial hours is but one of the hurdles to cross. There are sure to be clinical areas which are more difficult than others, so much so that the temptation to want to give up is very real.

To the Christian, the promise in 1 Thessalonians 5:24 'Faithful is He that calls you who will also do it', is the assurance that is required to go on and succeed in the most rewarding job you can have – caring.

Introduction

Once upon a time it might have been true that nursing was a respectable, genteel, ladylike occupation for dedicated single women. This is no longer so today. Hospitals are tough and demanding places to work in and nursing is not glamorous. Nevertheless, the rewards are enormous, and my desire is that – with God's help – this book will prove to be an encouragement to many Christians considering nursing as a career.

The delicate area of Christianity in our hospitals is dealt with in the final chapter. There I make clear the differing experiences of Christian nurses – about the helpfulness or unhelpfulness, the availability or invisibility – of hospital chapels and chaplains. I was aware as I wrote that the number of chaplains, both men and women, appears to be growing. This helped me to feel there might be greater opportunities ahead for cooperation as these good people strengthen the ranks of the Christian presence in our hospitals. Some of the more mature men and women entering this area of care come with deep experiences of their own to bring to their role of caring for patients as well as caring for staff.

For all Christian nurses already working in Britain's hospitals, you have my undying admiration. I hope that this book will prove to be a challenge and of some professional and spiritual value. My own experience as a patient in hospital and my involvement with the Nurses Christian Fellowship as editor of their magazine *Pacemaker*, plus the wise words of several mature Christian nurses which are contained in the following chapters, all helped to point to the truth. It is this: very young Christian nurses should aim for that spiritual maturity, in God's goodness, to equip them to be, only at the Holy Spirit's prompting, the ones to give spiritual care. However, that care should be given only when the patient asks for it – not because a Christian nurse decides he or she wants to 'convert' the patient.

I am deeply indebted to many Christian nurses for their help and advice. Without their encouragement this book might never have been completed. More important, Miss Ruth Bennett, RGN, RM, MTD, Senior Teacher, Royal College of Midwives, has been an invaluable professional watchdog, reading the draft to remove any errors.

Finally, I sincerely hope that *Called to Care?* will be of value to the youngsters who attend the NCF Summer Schools each year.

Mary Endersbee
February 1990

1

Prologue

'All the hairs on my arms would tingle with anticipation when I first went on the wards. I was in love with nursing – head over heels with it.'

Student Nurse Margaret Hayes

'I was appalled – all the observations made by me or my research assistants seemed to be saying we never actually plan nursing care for the individual needs of the patient.'

Professor Jean McFarlane

'During my first weeks I felt as if I was going from disaster to disaster. All my pride at reaching staff nurse grade quickly evaporated . . .'

Staff Nurse Kate

'Midwifery is not all emergencies – although there is something of the unknown with every delivery. I remember being little more than a shaking wreck with the first baby I delivered – and I still find the adrenaline keeps pumping until the placenta is out – every time . . .'

Midwife Gill Watts

'Gynaecology appears to be an ethical minefield; with abortion, the use and abuse of contraceptives; in vitro fertilisation, donor sperm, womb leasing and other methods to get round infertility . . .'

Senior Nurse Elizabeth

'Two or three weeks later they bring in this baby – fully dressed and ready to go home – and I hardly recognise the mother who is no longer distraught – or the baby who is no longer at death's door.'

Sister Polly

'I had always had this dream of becoming a clinical teacher – right from the start of my training as a nurse . . . I had no idea how many years it would take . . .'

Clinical Teacher Gill

'Working in the ITU with neonates was so stressful that many staff did not stay for more than two years . . .'

Sister Gill

'We had been so busy trying to keep her alive that we had failed to help her in her dying . . .'

Barbara Sinsen

'Hands on caring is less important than seeing if a variety of approaches can help them – you attempt to know the psychiatric patients as people not patients.'

Sister Beverley

'St Christopher's Hospice is about living as well as dying.'

Shirley du Boulay

'There is no doubt among those working in this field that the advent of AIDS represents an uniquely sinister threat to the human race . . .'

Robert J. Pratt, Head of Charing Cross
Hospital School of Nursing

'In trying to staff the new hospital she was aware that some sisters were so authoritarian she wondered which staff she could possibly ask to work on their wards.'

Senior Nurse Manager Elizabeth

'As a Christian I find it a privilege to be able to visit people at home and get involved with their families . . .'

District Nurse Marilyn

'The missionary nurse in the 1990s operates in a changing world. In many developing countries there is no longer a shortage of trained nurses . . .'

Laurence Dopson, Nursing Times

'I believe the Church has a definite function in nurturing and supporting people who are at the coal face of inter-action with human need.'

Baroness Jean McFarlane of Llandaff

2

The Changing Future of Nurse Education

'All the hairs on my arms would tingle with anticipation when I first went on the wards. I was in love with nursing – head over heels with it.'

Student Nurse Margaret Hayes

The training of nurses has changed as radically as has the profession of nursing itself. In the months since I began researching this book, the United Kingdom Central Council (nursing's official professional body), has authorised new titles for its nurses. Those who were known formerly as State Registered Nurses (SRN) are now to be entitled Registered General Nurses (RGN); those who were State Certified Midwives (SCM) are now to be called Registered Midwives (RM). The State Enrolled Nurse (SEN) is to be phased out altogether in future.

These changes are only a hint of the huge alterations affecting every aspect of nurse education. The three year RGN course will still be hospital based but each hospital is able to propose its own curriculum and practical programme for registration with the approval of the appropriate local Health Authority and National Board. Each country in the United Kingdom has its own National Board.

However, alongside hospitals, a new element has entered the equation – with Project 2000 student nurses have to be linked with a polytechnic or university because the courses will be on par with all other courses at diploma or degree level. This opens up greater opportunities for nursing students: if in future they want to do a further education based course – say in administration or management – they already have a recognised educational qualification. This should make nursing more attractive for those seeking a qualification within health care and a variety of learning experiences.

The proposed three year course offers a basic foundation programme for the first eighteen months. The second eighteen months will be in a more specialist branch programme chosen from four areas: adult, child, mental illness and mental handicap. Entry requirements for Project 2000 are still not clear as new types of course are being developed. But in 1989, fourteen health regions in England were asked to set up a Demonstration District for Project 2000. It is possible that some educational establishments may begin the new style nurse education in 1990.

New student status

Student status is to be given to nurses in training, and this will lead to one of the most major and revolutionary changes yet. Until very recently, the learners, the students, have provided a fifth of the workforce in hospitals. Due to the drop in the birth rate far fewer young school leavers will be recruited into nursing in any case, so the future staffing of the wards will become an even greater problem than it is today.

Some people in nursing have reacted strongly against the idea of the 'academic nurse'. All nurses with five O levels and a college based education is a proposal disturbing many. But we need to take a longer perspective on this. Rapid changes in technology, medical science and a new approach orientated towards health care rather than sickness, indicate the need for a new kind of nurse possessing good communication skills and the ability to cope with a rapidly changing work situation. It is worth bearing in mind that ward management today is lauded as a highly technical matter, and management skills have been presented as the essential requirements for ambitious staff wishing to move up the promotion ladder. This can create difficulties for the nurse who wants to concentrate on bedside care. Some ward sisters now have to manage budgets and ward accounts – not quite the type of skill one associates with dedicated bedside nursing and the Florence Nightingale image of old!

Degree courses for nurses

There are already, among our nursing workforce, many who have done the new degree courses. It is a revealing exercise to see how some of them have coped with the demands of the academic curriculum and the ward or hospital situations they have been faced with.

Sarah, who trained in London, was one of the first to do the new Bachelor of Science (SRN) degree. At her interview at a major London teaching hospital, when asked about her personal philosophy of life, she felt it right to mention the importance of her Christian faith. It did not count against her. She had done three A levels at school and had always considered the possibility of taking a nursing degree. From a very young age, she had wanted to be a nurse and to care for sick people. Her aim in applying to do the new degree was to be involved in the caring side and yet be stretched intellectually as well. She won one of only four places for the new course based partly in the hospital and partly in the new City University. It comprised a year's nursing, a year's social science, a third year half nursing and half social science and a thesis to be written in the fourth year. She recalls, 'We were pioneers – and thus we were very closely supervised.'

After only one week in the School of Nursing lecture hall, she went straight on to the wards, unlike the RGN students who usually do the eight week preliminary nursing training. The degree students had the advantage that the same tutor who taught them in the School also came and taught them clinical practice on the wards.

The hospital was an old-fashioned institution famous for its high standards. The first batch of degree students caused a good deal of misunderstanding. One sister asked Sarah, 'I suppose you're only going to do the dressings? You won't be spending any time in the sluice.' Thereafter, Sarah spent as much time in the sluice as she could. 'I wanted to prove to her that I was as willing to empty bedpans and wash bottles as anyone else.'

Another shock for the staff was the new reporting procedure. At the end of each ward allocation the student was to be shown the report the sister or staff nurse had written about them. This is normal practice now but fairly unusual then – the report was usually sent over to the School of Nursing and not shown to the student until later by someone else.

The shock for Sarah was her second year, her first university year. The contrast was enormous and she found the demands made upon her almost too much. She very nearly gave up altogether, partly because of the changed status and conditions under which she was working and living. Formerly she had been a hospital based student nurse – now she was a university student. In her first year, like other student nurses, she had lived in a nursing home; no male visitors were allowed in after 11 p.m., and she had eaten in the hospital dining room seated according to her rank.

Then in the second year, they moved out of the hospital accommodation to live in a fifteen floor tower block used as a student hostel – thirteen floors for men, two floors for women – and few regulations. She admitted it was a quite incredible contrast.

Furthermore Sarah discovered there were problems in marrying all the practical nursing with the more theoretic sociological and psychological theories they were studying. The final year included writing a thesis before returning to nursing and doing a special State registration paper, with a multiple-choice paper, an open book essay, care studies and four practical studies.

She qualified Bachelor of Science (Hons) and State Registered Nurse in 1972. The success of the experiment with degree courses was evident because the course grew each succeeding year and twelve students take it annually in her old hospital.

A second example of a degree student reveals the scope of entry for those not highly academically qualified. A nursing degree graduate from Manchester University, Robert came from the Lake District and was educated at a comprehensive school. In the Sixth Form with his O levels behind him, he decided suddenly that he wanted to do something vocational as a career. This was partly because he had come to a living faith in Jesus, and he had read about nursing in the school's career information. What helped to clarify his thinking and his Christian commitment was attending a summer school for would-be nurses, organised by the Nurses Christian Fellowship in Liverpool. No one in his family was a nurse and he had never been the sort who lived only for the day when he could become a nurse.

He discovered that while doing some hours of practical experience in his nearby geriatric hospital, and acquiring an A level, his impressions were not positive. Nevertheless, he still felt convinced that this was what God wanted him to do and he was accepted for the four year Bachelor of Nursing degree in Manchester. It was a Registered General Nurse course with extras! The first part of his course based him with an experienced district nurse in Salford. There Robert learned the benefits of seeing people as people, not just patients, living in their own homes and not in a hospital situation. He felt he had benefited especially from seeing how the community cared for its growing number of frail, elderly people.

Before that, he had spent a week at the university for introductory lectures, then spending one day a week in the community in his first term, the rest mainly in lectures. The second term was similar but hospital based, one day a week on the wards, the rest in lectures. The students moved around the various hospitals in Manchester during the course, so they had a wider experience than the usual RGN student.

As degree students the large number of hospital placements demanded a certain measure of adaptability. The only privilege otherwise was that they did very little night duty, unlike the other RGN students. Otherwise, on the ward there were no special privileges for the degree students. They were called student nurses and responsible to the sister of whichever ward they were on.

Academically, Robert found the four year degree course not at all easy. He discovered that being in a large institution was also very oppressive. The formality of the ward situation was quite difficult to adapt to and working there only one day a week meant it was harder to know exactly what was expected of him.

Unusually the Manchester Bachelor of Nursing degree at that time was an integrated one which qualified him also as a health visitor. The courses have tended to vary in content over the years of experimentation. Not all students doing the later Manchester degree would necessarily qualify in the same way.

The Nursing Process described in Chapter 3 is now so accepted in nursing that it will occur in this book in a number of different chapters. Indeed, Manchester University is famous in nursing circles for the work and research done by Professor Jean McFarlane, a leading expert in the field and a Christian of many years' standing. Professor Jean has recently retired, but she was responsible for pioneering one of the most significant changes in nursing practice. Added to which she has had the rare distinction of becoming the first nurse to be a member of the House of Lords.

Graduate nurses

Alongside those who become graduates as part of their nursing training, a special effort is being made to attract graduates into nursing. With the current shortage of school leavers, it is timely to offer new and shortened courses for more mature entrants. Many teaching hospitals and polytechnics offer places to graduates to do a special RGN adapted to their needs. Usually the course is shortened by four months or more, with at least one less ward placement.

Emphasis on community care

The UKCC, the overall body responsible for steering through these new professional changes in nurse education, has achieved considerable progress already. In 1989 there were several innovative demonstration nursing schools in operation with this new emphasis on student status for its learners – and upon nurses seeing their work in the context of the community. Gone are the days when the nurse trained for three years in a ward situation only then to be allowed to work as a district nurse in the local community – after they had qualified as SRNs and done some further training.

The necessity for an understanding of community care early on in a nurse's education is explained by the needs of Britain's increasingly ageing population and improvements in medical treatment which mean people stay in hospital for shorter periods than previously, going home to complete their recovery.

At the moment, the nurses who usually work in the community are district nurses, midwives, community psychiatric nurses backed up by health visitors and practice nurses who are linked to GP clinics or health centres, not hospitals. Most of these have had to qualify separately after finishing their three year hospital training.

Coping with the staff

Not only does a student or graduate nurse face the demands of a new academic syllabus, totally different often from what they have done previously, but also they have to learn to cope with the staff – tutors, sisters, staff nurses and clinical teachers.

Most nurses have one or two horror stories to tell of particularly difficult situations when they were training with very demanding staff. The number of students (and staff nurses) who hide in the sluice or the linen cupboard to avoid a difficult sister seems to be immense. Some will not finish the course at all because of the way they have been treated by the staff. Beverley, who had always wanted to be a nurse, ran into total disaster in her first year of her General Nursing course in Hampshire. She failed to make the grade and was made to feel there was no future for her in nursing – which as it happened proved incorrect.

She felt she had very little support from the trained staff and that the ward situation was too hierarchical. 'I could not get any encouragement. The sister did not speak to the students – she just shouted at us. The staff nurses were awful – just sat in the office and did nothing. The students were left to do all the nursing care.'

With hindsight, Beverley believes she should have stood up for herself instead of letting the sister tell her that she was worse than useless and would never make a nurse. What made it worse was that the sister sent a report to that effect to the School of Nursing, and Beverley's confidence crumbled completely. Not surprisingly, she left. Despite that unpromising start, she became a qualified nurse later. After doing some auxiliary nursing in a different kind of hospital she realised her real niche was in psychiatric nursing. She qualified as a Registered Mental Nurse in three years and went on to hold responsible positions up to sister in various acute psychiatric wards in London and the Midlands.

She says she loves psychiatric nursing for the very

freedoms not allowed on the general nursing wards when
she started her training. There is less hierarchy in staff
relationships, no uniform and Christian names are used,
while one to one relationships with patients are encouraged. 'Everybody's opinion matters and is valued in a
psychiatric ward – it is a lot more relaxed and friendly than
on the general wards. Even as a student your views and
ideas matter in the weekly meetings and you feel an important part of the multidisciplinary team.'

There are always going to be the negative experiences
in nursing to set against the positive. It would be dishonest
not to mention the dropouts and those who do not complete their courses. There are many pressures on a student
nurse and nursing calls for a high degree of personal
commitment. Self-discipline and hard work are essential
to complete the various practical and theoretical aspects
of the courses.

Some hospitals make an effort to provide a carer to look
after their student nurses, but this is certainly not true of
all.

Christian nurse learners speak appreciatively of the
tremendous support and joy it is to share with another
Christian their problems – for prayer or mutual support.
This is partly why hospital Christian fellowships and Nurses
Christian Fellowships can be vitally important. But the
Church plays a major role also. Some ministers, recognis-
ing that like policemen nurses have to work shifts, make
special efforts to help nurses feel wanted and involved even
when they cannot attend church every Sunday morning.

Job satisfaction

Many Christians in nursing acknowledge enormous job
satisfaction, which is the added ingredient not always apparent when reading official information related to courses
and options. One student nurse doing her PTS, Preliminary
Training School, was so excited when she first went on the
wards that all the hairs on her forearms would tingle with

anticipation. 'I was in love with nursing – head over heels with it.' And she was not disappointed either. She only recently retired after more than forty years in the profession, most of it spent overseas as a missionary nurse and midwife, training national Christians to be community midwives latterly in West Africa.

She had no regrets, finding nursing not only excellent training in all dimensions but also good for her own self-discipline and for the development of emotional strength. She discovered that, despite wartime upheavals and many privations abroad, she felt so fulfilled by her work that she never wanted to do anything else.

Another nurse, Jo, came into nursing late. She had done a Business Studies degree in the Midlands, followed by a management course with Marks and Spencer. Feeling that was not for her, and praying that God would guide, the door into nursing unexpectedly opened.

Nursing was a total contrast, and she had to admit there were some aspects which she found particularly hard to cope with.

'I found my first ward experiences very frightening. You have absolutely no idea what to expect or what is expected of you. I found that hard possibly because I was not eighteen – I had been used to being in an office environment where I had a lot of responsibility and took the initiative.'

Even in a few months she had seen the negative aspect of nursing with wards opening and closing due to financial cutbacks. But it was her first spell on a geriatric ward that came as a big shock to her system. It was called Care of the Elderly, which is the new and better name for this ward. But she felt some of the care the people were getting was appalling. She watched in horror as one student gave an old lady a bed bath as if she were a lump of meat, with no attempt at maintaining the patient's dignity.

She discovered it was learning to cope with people's bodies that she found most demanding. This was especially true in that Care of the Elderly ward. 'Some bodies were twisted totally – or wasted away – others had terrible pressure sores. Some had neglected themselves terribly before being admitted to hospital, and were very smelly . . .' At one point, in utter despair, she cried out inwardly, 'Lord, what on earth am I doing here? I can't handle bodies!'

As she went home that night, fretting that she had made a big mistake and feeling she could not cope any longer, she prayed very hard. She had become a Christian during her student years. Now she asked God to reassure her about bodies. Should she really be back in a nice office job, relating to people's minds instead of their bodies?

'The more I prayed, the more I suddenly realised that all the body was is a home for that person and their spirit. As long as you can look at that person as a person – and see inside – then that body becomes irrelevant. The job of the nurse is to make sure that the body is functioning in the best possible way – and the person inside that body is as comfortable as they can be. I realised I had to relate to the person inside the body, and it helped to take away from what you can immediately see.'

For Jo, this was a breakthrough in her nursing career. She still had to cope with caring for people with twisted, curled up limbs or deformed and revolting feet, but she no longer found it so difficult. 'This experience has changed me radically in ways that I am so thankful for. It has made me see people as individuals. Nursing has taught me the value of people – and I believe nursing is the best thing I have ever done!'

3

A Revolution in Patient Care

*'I was appalled – all the observations made by me or
my assistants seemed to be saying we never actually plan
nursing care for the individual needs of the patient . . .'*
Professor Jean McFarlane

Possibly the biggest revolution affecting Britain's hospitals
concerns the patients themselves more than the nurses.
Gone are most of the vast regimented, ether- or carbolic-
permeated and impersonal wards of the past. In most
hospitals, large wards are divided into several smaller ten
bed bays which are attractively decorated and run on more
flexible and humane lines. Patients are usually made to
feel their personal needs matter *more* than the ward routine. Much of this has come about as a result of applying
the 'Nursing Process', a relatively new holistic approach
to patient care.

The rigid ward routine of the past, partly inherited from
Florence Nightingale, had its right and proper place when
many more patients stayed in hospital for longer periods.
It mattered especially when aseptic techniques were far
less satisfactory and cross-infection and septicaemia, the
great fear which haunted ward sisters, could cause fatalit-
ies. The maternity wards of the past were just one such
area of risk. Before penicillin and antibiotics were
available, many mothers-to-be faced the horror of losing

their babies or their own lives through becoming infected after admission to the labour ward itself. All the washing and wiping and the boiling and sterilising were not totally without point. The old-fashioned ward routine did provide a great sense of security, too – for patients as well as staff. Everyone knew their place in the daily ritual of feeding and cleansing the bodies in the beds. However, as medical knowledge has grown and modern technology has helped to shorten many patients' course of hospital treatment there is less necessity for such rigid practices.

Standards of care

There is more to this gentle revolution than that, of course. Cleanliness does not always indicate a high standard of care. It took major academic research into standards of hospital care in the United Kingdom to help bring home to the nursing profession that standards of care were not what they should be. The former Professor of Nursing at Manchester University, Jean McFarlane, now Baroness McFarlane of Llandaff, was one of the leading figures in this crucial research.

Until 1988 Jean McFarlane was Professor of Nursing at Manchester, in a major teaching role which she had held since 1971. She was able to influence many nursing students not only at the university but also in the various hospitals around the city. She is no mere ivory-tower academic, however. She has worked close to much social deprivation in several major cities in Britain.

Her childhood home was Cardiff in South Wales, her father a general practitioner. Her first choice of degree course on leaving school was chemistry and that took her to Bedford College, London, in 1945-6. Besides her studies Jean met some 'fairly lively Christians associated with the Inter-Varsity Fellowship'. She came from a Christian family but church at home appeared somewhat joyless in comparison. In London she also met for the first time Christians who believed God could change people's lives instantly and she witnessed God answering prayer, partly through the work carried out by the London Embankment Mission.

Jean decided that Christianity worked and chemistry and test tubes were not for her. She was attracted by missionary work, too, and had been attending prayer meetings held at the China Inland Mission and at the Middlesex Hospital. One way forward in order to be a missionary was to become a nurse, she felt. She applied to five London teaching hospitals and decided to train at the first one to offer her a place – St Bartholomew's (Barts) in 1947. She had great reservations still. 'But I knew this was something that the Lord wanted me to do. I felt he was calling me to do this. And that was a tremendous motivating force – and a consolation in the ups and downs of my career.' In fact, she felt very comfortable at Barts and very safe and secure in the firm discipline. But there was one major drawback to hospital nursing: the shifts and duty rotas meant she could get to church only rarely, and there was no fellowship for the nurses in the hospital at that time. She wanted to be freer to attend church regularly and decided one way to do this was to become a health visitor.

Over a period of time she had become interested in the preventive aspect of medicine. Several patients she nursed on one ward had diabetes mellitus. In those days, they would come into hospital to be balanced up, then sent home again. A few weeks later the same patients would have to be readmitted with gangrene or a dangerous level of blood sugar. Jean was convinced that the preventive aspect of nursing care was the better way of treating diabetics by improving care at home, by educating the patient and his family about diet, etc. Health visiting she knew could be one way of supporting such cases and possibly keeping them from being admitted to hospital at all.

During the Second World War, certain wards at Barts were evacuated to Hill End, St Albans. The hospital was not far from St Albans Abbey. 'One of the pictures that I carry in my memory from that time was of three of the

sisters who used to go off every morning to Communion
at the Abbey before they came on duty. I used to see them
cycling up the drive with their long tunnelled white caps
flowing in the breeze behind them. Somehow it was a
recognition that that Communion was where they got their
strength from for the duties ahead. That impressed me.'

There were notable nursing figures who impressed her
also. Helen Day was Matron and surprised Jean by knowing her name when passing her in the Square one day.
Considering the huge number of nurses and students at
Barts this was quite an achievement. Winifred Hector was
one of her tutors. Miss Hector insisted on wearing a sister's
blue uniform, not a tutor's, saying, 'I wear this because
there is no greater calling in nursing than to be a ward
sister and to manage the clinical care of patients.'

'Even in those days she was sowing the idea in my mind
that, if you ever teach nursing – you cannot afford to be
far away from clinical practice.' Some of that certainly
guided Jean's own approach in Manchester where she
refused to be lecture room oriented but relied on plenty
of clinical practice for herself with the students in the
nearby hospitals.

After qualifying as a State Registered Nurse in 1950,
Jean stayed at Barts as a staff nurse for a year, then applied
to do midwifery. She knew this would be necessary for her
to become a health visitor. She took her Part I Midwifery
back home in Cardiff, then Part II in Hereford.

Health visiting

One of the big disappointments that Jean discovered when
she moved back to Cardiff to do the health visitor's course
was that the focus was almost exclusively on mother and
child health. So she did not move into preventive care as
fast as she had hoped. Nonetheless there were encouraging
signs. They were just beginning to experiment with health
visitor specialists for such areas as diabetes, asthma,
cardiac care and TB. Once she was practising, she eventu-

ally became such a specialist with BCG vaccinations for TB, which took her into all the schools in Cardiff doing Mantoux testing and giving vaccinations to the children during her final two years as a health visitor.

There was some excitement in the air over her research findings. The results of the new vaccination programme in the 1950s were quite dramatic. When she first started testing in the schools about 80 or 90 per cent of the children would be Mantoux positive – not vaccinated against TB. Only a few years later, after the course of vaccinations, it was down to only 5 per cent! And that proved to be the national trend.

This work introduced Jean to the epidemiological method – the study of an epidemic in a population now more broadly used to study any medical trend in a population. It was a vitally useful piece of research which had taken her into homes all over the city. If the children's tests proved positive Jean had to visit their homes to discover who was the TB carrier. Then those with TB were sent for X-rays and into hospital for treatment, especially if it was what was known as 'open TB'. Covering the whole of Cardiff meant visiting some tough areas. She met with some tragic and deprived mothers and families whose needs she found herself praying over and discussing especially with her father who knew well some of the social deprivations of the city.

Research and teaching

At home in Cardiff several new elements impressed themselves on her in the 1950s and helped to move her on into research and teaching – both vital elements of her future pioneering work with the Nursing Process.

For a start, at the Welsh School of Medicine in Cardiff there was a tutor who was to have a great influence on Jean's career. Through Mary Davies, her tutor on the health visitor's course and 'a woman of great vision about nursing', Jean became secretary to the Public Health section. Soon she was chairman and secretary of the Cardiff branch too, while still working as a health visitor. 'It was in this way that I got a broader view of nursing and nursing politics then.' Finally, she was elected on to the Central Committee of the Public Health section of the Royal College of Nursing in London.

Mary Davies then suggested that Jean should help her with her teaching of health visitors. Jean resisted quite strongly because all her family were teachers. She gave in eventually and discovered that she enjoyed the course, which was unusually go ahead. It was taught in the department of preventive medicine and they had joint lectures with doctors who were doing the Diploma in Public Health and with students from the social science course.

Not only did Jean find herself lecturing about the BCG work and the results of the Mantoux tests, she also started to have her work published. While working with a doctor who was a community physician, she was helped by him to write up her research in such a way that their papers from the joint research project were published in *The Lancet* in 1956-57. This was a great source of satisfaction.

As a result of all this Jean returned to London to train as a tutor herself at the RCN in 1959 at Cavendish Square. In her Bible on that occasion she marked this turning point in her career and the date. Having prayed about this new departure 'to me it was the hand of the Lord saying – yes, this teaching is something I want you to do. I can look back to that note in the margin and recall the day I started my teaching career. It proved to be a marvellous year, in any case, of learning and it was a very interesting course. There were other Christians among the students. In fact, hospital administrators and tutors from all over the world were on it, too, so it had a truly international flavour.'

However, she discovered that health visiting and preventive medicine were still considered the poor relations. Those doing the hospital admin. or hospital tutor's courses were regarded as being vastly superior to the health visitors. Jean longed for that to change.

Among their lecturers, Norah Mackenzie was outstanding on ethics and education, a whole new field for Jean. Elaine Wilkie, another Christian nurse, was the course tutor, and later preceded Jean into her job at Manchester. She was pioneering a new education programme there. Little did Jean realise she was one day to follow in her footsteps.

First however she took on Elaine's teaching role at the RCN. 'Thus, one day in July 1957 I was a student at the RCN, the next I was on the staff as tutor in the Education Division.' She enjoyed it very much and found tremendous fulfilment in teaching health visitors. She bought a home in Putney, too, and shared it with a niece who was at Roehampton. She began to attend a church in Denmark Hill and made many new friends.

Already there are pointers ahead – the college introduced an integrated course with King's College, London University. Later, in Birmingham and Manchester she was to run the same kind of integrated courses for the first time.

In fact, Jean's first move was north to Birmingham as education officer of the RCN Centre, teaching just such an integrated health visitor's course. The post was demanding and challenging as she was asked to plan and organise short refresher courses for all kinds of nursing personnel – for anyone from a male nurse from a psychiatric hospital to a theatre sister or staff from general or maternity hospitals. The courses usually lasted a week or a fortnight and she had to bring all her students up to date in their own special subjects. Thus, she had to cover a very wide spectrum of knowledge, had to plan the programme, ask people to lecture and do a good deal of lecturing herself. She also spent a good deal of her time visiting local firms and other important industrial companies around the city. By this time she had made a new home for herself in Erdington, sharing it with her widowed mother.

Among her courses at the Centre, Jean was proud to be pioneering something new – and proving its relevance,

too. They ran the first Care of the Elderly course which
attracted so many people – seventy – that it had to be
repeated twice a year thereafter. It was designed for all
sorts of health professionals – those working in the community as well as those working in hospitals. Next they
pioneered the first course in Programmed Learning – and
on Research Methods in Nursing. These were two totally
new areas for nurse education and the latter course was to
lead her on to higher things. This was partly thanks to one
of Jean's guest lecturers on Research Methods – a former
research officer at the London RCN, Marjorie Simpson.
In the light of all the new ground Jean had been breaking
in Birmingham, it was not surprising that Marjorie con-
founded her with a startling request: 'Jean, we are wanting
to mount a very large project on the quality of nursing
care. Will you come back to London and be in charge of
it?'

Jean had been very happy in Birmingham, and had even
registered for an evening class course in 1964 at Aston
University to gain a Bachelor of Sociology degree. She
was not easily persuaded. But her arguments against the
move ended when she was promised a year off to complete
her degree. They still wanted her very much as so few
nurses had a degree or knew anything about research
methods.

London and the research project

She returned to her former college, Bedford College, and
completed her course at Aston in 1965, gaining a Bachelor
of Sociology degree. In 1966 she took up her new role as
Research Officer at the RCN in charge of the project
aimed at assessing standards of care and formulating ways
of assessing the quality of care. She had to build up the
whole thing from scratch and she employed six research
assistants to bring back their findings for collation and
assessment. Each assistant spent a month in various wards
in teaching hospitals around London, purely as observers

and studying different aspects of care. It was not an easy time. Jean was appalled by their findings about standards of care. In the two years she spent on that research project her whole life was changed.

All the observations made by me or my assistants seemed to be saying, we never actually plan nursing care for the individual needs of the patient. Nursing is so routinised that the patient care does not meet individual need. This realisation became a kind of obsession with me. I knew we had to do something about this discovery.

It was then I realised you could not alter the methods of nursing care unless you altered the education of future nurses. Because the reason why we had a routinised approach to care was that we had been educated as nurses to do it that way. We had to change not only the system of care but also the education for that system.

When Jean first made known the results of her research and her conclusions at the RCN, there was a major row over any proposed changes in nursing care or nursing education. It was going to take much more time and a great deal more research to bring about what Jean saw as an essential change of attitude in nursing. She was then appointed Director of Education at the RCN in London and set aside for the moment her research project. The year was 1968, and she returned to the high-powered world of nursing politics and discovered the broader relations that had to be maintained between the RCN and the Department of Health and Social Security, major professional bodies such as the General Nursing Council and the Central Midwives Board, and the Department of Education and Science. In her position at the hub of nurse education her obsession could be shared with her colleagues more fully. It also allowed her time to do a Master of Science degree at Birkbeck College, London, on manpower studies.

Manchester

When Jean MacFarlane took up a post as Professor of
Nursing at Manchester University in 1971, all her varied
academic qualifications and wide experience plus her
concern for improving standards of care enabled her to
introduce revolutionary changes in nurse education.

> One of the first things we worked on in the undergrad-
> uate programme was . . . making sure that nursing
> theory and practice were integrated. Then in 1972, I
> read the first paper sharing my findings when I had
> analysed what nursing is and the kind of decisions nurses
> have to make. This led on to what became known as
> The Nursing Process – a decision-making process which
> included gathering data on the patient, making an assess-
> ment of that data then planning the care of each patient
> individually, and finally evaluation of the progress
> achieved.

The Nursing Process is still regarded today as an essential
part of most nurses' training – though not all. It trains
nurses to plan their care with the needs of the individual
patient in mind and involves (a) assessment of the individual; (b) identification of the nursing problems; (c) making
a plan of care that caters for those problems; (d) carrying
out that care and (e) evaluating that care.

There was yet a further stage for this new method to be
proved acceptable. Professor Jean McFarlane started by
implementing her Nursing Process education programme
in Manchester. Then, after a visit to Manchester in 1978
by the then General Nursing Council, came the highest
accolade she could be awarded. A directive was issued
stating that nursing should be taught using the Nursing
Process as in Manchester. Jean thanked God that her
particular concern with improving nursing care seemed to
have met a real need; and succeeded, despite its emphasis
on caring for individuals, in an increasingly secular and
technology-orientated age.

Other views of the Nursing Process

Older nurses who were trained before the inception of the Nursing Process can be somewhat offhand about it. 'Suddenly,' said one sister, 'we had to start remembering to write down all these things about each patient. And the students knew more than we did. That can be pretty threatening to a sister not trained in the Nursing Process. It seemed to me we had managed to work perfectly well without it all those years. We did not see any need for it. The patients were not getting any better care through the new system – so I am not over enthusiastic.'

Another Christian nurse, now working in the community, felt differently. 'In the old system, with strict ward routines, the patients were cowed. They must not mess up Sister's neat clean ward. Nurses were not allowed to sit on patients' beds or talk to patients as individuals – that was considered as wasting time. Everything was regimented.' But since the introduction of the Nursing Process she felt that there was a much better atmosphere in hospitals today. Instead of keeping wards clean and tidy, routines are geared more to the patient and his needs. 'I am much happier with the more patient-oriented treatment. It was certainly not done in the past to talk to the patient about their personal faith either. Now it seems spiritual care matters – it is part of this holistic approach. This approach is my heart's desire – as a Christian – to meet the *whole* needs of my patients, not just the physical but all the other aspects.' However, she did not believe the nurses had to have been taught the Nursing Process to be aware of a patient's individual needs.

A Christian sister in psychiatric nursing gave the Nursing Process top marks. She saw it as very important in psychiatry, the patients' needs being paramount.

We have to plan the patients' care. First we identify their problems before we can plan their care and sort out how we are going to implement it. You need some plan of assessment and actions such as the Nursing Process provides.

Normally we see patients for the first time when we admit them and we give them a three day assessment and meet together to decide what their problems are then and where we are going to go with them. Before the Nursing Process came along, I think care was a lot more haphazard. Now we give individualised care and I think that is great. The patients are people – not identical objects on a conveyor belt. Though it makes for more paper work, I like it. We need to keep patients' care plans up to date each time they are evaluated. I think the care plans for psychiatric patients are not as straightforward as they may be in General nursing, because the patients' needs are not so straightforward.

It is clear there is some variation around the country as to how wholeheartedly hospitals and schools of nursing have adopted the Nursing Process. Individual nurses, too, vary in their assessment. One West Indian junior sister working in a London hospital admitted that though she appreciated its holistic approach to the patient, when she trained in 1983-7, the nursing school seemed to have heard little about it.

It is still a new idea to many nurses where I work – even in 1989 they really do not know how it works – even if it was first introduced in the 1970s. A lot of tutors have not come to grips with it. Our hospital now provides a course in the School of Nursing, but that only came into operation in 1987.

Though basically the emphasis is to treat each patient as a whole, and not just a set of symptoms, you still get regimented wards due to lack of staff and no time to spend on patient care. It also depends on the sister and on the pressure of work on a big ward when you are always short-staffed. You then revert to the list of jobs to be done – the basic jobs of keeping patients fed and washed – and there is no time for anything else in the rush to complete that. Then, too, there are the sisters who prefer to stick to the old-fashioned ways and say – 'we've always been doing this this way – why the need to change?'

But even when we try to bring in a more patient-oriented system, the Nursing Process takes up a lot of the nurse's time writing reports. You have all these forms to fill in – information sheets, assessment forms, care plans, etc. As we are permanently understaffed, we have been unable to implement fully all that the Nursing Process entails.

However, one midwife tutor disagrees. She believes it is not the paperwork that takes time. It is the fact that nurses are actually listening more to the patients as individuals which is time-consuming and can prove a problem when the turnover of patients is so rapid nowadays.

For the Christian nurse and midwife the key issue is still that each person is an individual made by God with differing hopes, fears and aspirations. Any method which can help to recognise that individuality and respond to it is valuable, and Christian professionals need to go on exploring ways of increasing understanding.

4

Staff Nurse Blues

'During my first weeks I felt as if I was going from
disaster to disaster. All my pride at reaching Staff Nurse
grade quickly evaporated . . .'

Staff Nurse Kate

Most teaching hospitals if they are short-staffed require
newly qualified staff - staff nurses - to remain with them
for a set number of months. The end of a nurse's training
is therefore a somewhat fraught time of decision making
about the future, making job applications, studying for
hospital finals – and the State finals – as well as deciding
whether to go on to take midwifery, which used to be the
norm for every nurse.

For Christian nurse students, praying about this decision
helps enormously to relieve some of the pressure, and
being able to share the problems with other Christians in
the hospital or at their church can also help.

Being a staff nurse can turn out to be very different from
what one had imagined. Kate, a Christian working in a big
London hospital, expressed some of the shattered dreams
she experienced as a new staff nurse and explained how
God met with her in that situation.

At the end of my first three months as a staff nurse I
found myself forced to reflect on the transition from

student to staff nurse. Throughout my training I awaited the day when I could call myself 'Staff Nurse' with great anticipation. I was so keen to assume this title that I cycled to buy the Petersham belt and attached my buckle before my first shift, when I knew I had passed the exams. I can remember proudly wearing my belt and staff nurse's badge full of confidence until disaster occurred and I was left feeling as inadequate as ever.

It was that first day that I realised being a staff nurse did not mean that I had changed at all; it was just that other people's perceptions of me had changed. Visitors to the ward and student nurses, doctors, etc., seemed to focus on my belt and think that I could answer their many queries. People seemed suddenly to view me as a multi-disciplinary expert; even the ward domestic seemed to think I could break into the broom cupboard when she locked her keys and handbag in!

All this new found responsibility came as a bit of a shock to me. I had to learn so many new things about ward management as well as being responsible for the patients and students. During my first few weeks I felt as if I was going from disaster to disaster and began to wonder whether I would ever quite make a proper staff nurse. All my pride at reaching the staff nurse grade quickly evaporated and a feeling of inadequacy took over.

My gloom was not helped by low staff numbers, a heavy workload and a distinct lack of positive feedback. I learned how rarely people say anything positive – it always seems easier to complain. 'Thank you' have become very valuable words to me – ones not used often enough. It is very easy too to get caught up in other people's arguments and end up involved in a never ending cycle of negativity.

At first, I used to become quite upset that no one ever said anything nice to me. It felt like being in the centre of a dart board with darts coming from all directions. Gradually I am learning that following God's will is

more important than praise from other people. I am
beginning to feel more confident in my own ability – and
so do not spend every waking minute worrying whether
or not Sister is going to be pleased with me when she
returns from her days off! I know that I have still got
a lot to learn and so constructive criticism is always
welcome.

One thing I had not bargained for is being so tired. I
seem to spend most of my time feeling totally empty,
collapsed in a heap trying to muster the energy for the
next shift. There have been times when I have felt totally
empty, no more left to give. It is at these moments
when God has really carried me through. Luke's Gospel
chapter 11 verses 5-13 have been especially valuable –
'Ask and it will be given you, seek and you will find,
knock and the door will be opened to you . . .' remind-
ing me what the Lord will give me, if only I would ask.
Isaiah 40 verses 28-31 are another reminder of how the
Lord sustains us when human energy fails. Indeed, the
Lord has never given me more than I can cope with in His
strength but He clearly shows me my own limitations.

But shattered dreams are by no means the experience of
all new staff nurses. Another London based new staff
nurse, Margaret, was fortunate to work on the ward of her
choice when she qualified – the children's ward. 'I applied
to work on that ward because I had worked there as a
student and loved it. I knew the ward, I knew the sister
and I enjoyed nursing sick children. I liked the sister in
fact, which is quite important. There were two wards, in
fact, of twenty beds each and I shared the duties with a
strong staff team – usually Sister, three or four staff nurses,
a nursery nurse and maybe six or seven students to a ward.'

Sadly, however, this number of staff is not typical. Often
wards are constantly short-staffed and only maintained by
agency nurses.

Opting for her second choice and hoping later to work
on the ward she preferred was Staff Nurse Polly. It took

far longer than she imagined to reach her goal. Polly trained in Sheffield as a State Registered Children's Nurse, then chose to do midwifery in Leicester – eventually she hoped to nurse neonates (babies who have problems at birth).

Before I finished my midwifery year I already knew I wanted to return to children's nursing. So I applied for a staff nurse post advertised on one of the children's medical wards. I had always much preferred surgical – but I felt it was right to take what I could and so I applied. In fact I had the interview the same day as my midwifery finals, having hung on and hung on still hoping a job on the surgical ward might become vacant. I was actually offered the staff nurse's job on the medical ward there and then. So I took it believing I might ask to be transferred if a vacancy occurred on the surgical ward.

In the end I did fifteen months as a staff nurse on that medical ward and actually discovered I enjoyed it because – probably – I was gaining my confidence a little. But it helped me enormously that I knew some of the other staff were Christians too so that we could share our problems and support each other.

Student nurse Jackie, training in London, had the unnerving experience of failing her State finals while passing her hospital exams. She had become engaged in her final year so there were distractions. But she still recalled her sense of shock. 'It was like a slap in the face. I just expected to pass the State Registered finals. We were all destined to become staff nurses anyway – whether we passed our SRN or not. But we were not allowed to receive the full uniform until we had passed it. The staff nurse's cap and belt were given – but not the full uniform badge. I had to resit the finals and pass them before that.'

It makes an enormous difference to any new staff nurse to discover helpful staff on a new ward. In an ideal staffing situation, the Key Nurse system is organised by go-ahead sisters, especially in teaching hospitals. Sister Esther, for instance, working in a big London hospital, operates such a scheme: 'We use a Key Nurse system whereby each staff nurse is responsible for two or three students. We try to work it too that the student nurse does night duty with the staff nurse who is her key nurse. When new staff arrive and are attached to one of the staff nurses, this gives the latter individual responsibility and they write the intermediate reports on the students and help to write their final report.'

Sister Esther also organises a monthly staff meeting lasting at least an hour where all the staff can discuss ward issues and problems. She welcomes from students and staff nurses suggestions to improve ward efficiency. Sometimes the students make a suggestion which the senior staff think will not work, but Esther believes it is often better that they discuss it and experiment for themselves to find out if it will work. She tries to make herself available also to help any staff or students who are finding things difficult.

Becoming a staff nurse brings responsibility not only for patients but also for their families. No nurse can concentrate on patient care without looking after distressed relatives. Often the distraught families of seriously ill patients demand as much time and attention as those in bed.

Sister Jane, working in a major teaching hospital in London, remembers how one poor staff nurse 'copped it' in no uncertain terms from the relative of one of her patients. Jane was then a fairly new sister of a neurology ward and in her new role was still learning about building relationships with patients' families. One eminent public figure was admitted with a tumour on the brain which seriously affected his balance. His wife was having a difficult time accepting the full implications of her husband's illness. He would keep falling over which caused her to become extremely agitated and almost unable to cope. Her anxiety manifested itself in angry outbursts at the staff.

She insisted he had a single room though the staff could not keep a constant eye on him in a small side ward and each time he had a fall she got very cross. One day he asked to use the commode and the staff nurse who was supposed to remain with him was ordered out of the room. One of his legs would not function properly and he fell off the commode. He did not hurt himself but his wife chose that moment to arrive. In loud and angry tones she castigated the staff and especially the staff nurse who had left him untended. Later Sister Jane was able to calm his wife and eventually she wrote Jane a lovely letter of thanks for her care of her husband.

Another staff nurse, in doing her duty towards one female patient on a very strict diet, was called all the names under the sun. Discovered by her downstairs in the snack bar eating food certainly not allowed on her strict diet, the patient vehemently denied eating the food. She then became extremely angry, accusing the staff nurse of telling tales behind her back. The ward sister eventually persuaded her to see sense. It entailed spending considerable time with the patient and allowing her space to talk over some of her deeper problems. The sister had to comfort the staff nurse too.

Teamwork relies on the willingness to work with a wide variety of people from all sorts of cultures and backgrounds – particularly in multiracial Britain. Many nurses from the West Indies work in our hospitals. Not all of them have had happy experiences. Some of them speak of racist attitudes among other members of staff. Carole from Jamaica, whose home is in Yorkshire, met with problems from a white staff nurse in her training in Rotherham. Instead of helping her the staff nurse seemed determined to make Carole suffer, especially on one ward where Carole was the only black student.

'It was awful,' said Carole, 'I couldn't do anything right – so much so that it nearly went to disciplinary action. My main support was my Christian friends at church – and my mum who is also a Christian and a midwife. I kept pouring out my problems to my mum, and my church were all praying for me that somehow I would stick it out and cope – and I did.'

It transpired that the staff nurse had just failed to get her promotion to sister. The sister of the ward was black and it was due to her report that the girl was not successful.

Staff Nurse Alice is Singapore Chinese. When she came to work in the United Kingdom, her problem was that she had to accept a post on a ward not of her choosing – an ophthalmology ward that she did not enjoy.

'You see I love bedside nursing and it was a surgical ward – and in eye surgery the turnover of patients is so fast that you do not get to know the patients properly.' Eventually she became a staff nurse on the ward of her choice, an oncology ward treating terminally ill cancer patients. It was a huge ward of seventy-three beds, divided up into three separate bays.

When I first went on that big ward I was very, very frightened. But I found it a great training and being there helped to conquer my fear. There was plenty of bedside care needed too and I really enjoyed giving that and getting to know each patient. One special joy was that I was known as a committed Christian, and if the patients wanted spiritual care or counsel, the other staff always called me over. They felt I could give the patients better pastoral care than they could.

To conclude this chapter on being a staff nurse, we move to Leicester and discover a young nurse thrown in at the deep end on a large, very busy geriatric ward dogged by staff shortages. The NHS is having great problems in recruiting staff, and Staff Nurse Janet's experiences are not untypical.

Janet trained at a major London teaching hospital where they were encouraged to stay for six months at least. She staffed on a general medical ward.

I enjoyed that – it was a really good experience with a lot of haematology and diabetic patients. But, next, I applied to do midwifery, thinking one day I may want to go overseas as a missionary nurse and midwife. The course I applied to do in Leicester was postponed and meanwhile I had to do something. So I took a job at a small geriatric hospital in Leicester as a staff nurse. There were six wards of twenty-eight beds each. But I found working there very frustrating. This was chiefly because I was the youngest staff member by some years. Also, having been there the shortest time, when Sister decided to go off to do a course [as staff are often encouraged to do], I ended up being the only staff nurse and thus Acting Sister. That was a bit of a strain . . . But it was excellent experience and very good for me.

The greatest test she discovered was not the patients but the staff. It was a longstay geriatric hospital and many of the auxiliary staff had been there for a very long time – like some of the patients. The staff seemed to have lost interest in the job. It was very heavy work too with a lot of lifting of senile or disabled patients. It was even harder work when there were only six staff on duty to do it. Often there was a lack of respect for patients, evident for example in staff not bothering to draw the curtains round a patient's bed when giving a bed bath or treating bedsores; or lugging people singlehandedly out of beds or chairs as if they were lumps of meat. Although this lack of proper care was caused chiefly by shortage of staff, there was another reason.

The previous sister had run the ward on somewhat rigid and regimented lines, but under the present sister it had begun to be more relaxed: she wanted patients to be treated as individuals, she made changes, popular with the patients but opposed by the long entrenched and overworked staff. Janet worked hard to maintain the more humane approach, and said that she learnt a great deal that was of value in the eleven months she spent there, as the new changes in ward procedure and practice gradually began to take effect. As a staff nurse Janet was in a position to influence significantly the atmosphere and attitudes of staff towards patients in her ward. As a Christian, it was her desire to enable her elderly patients to be treated with dignity.

5

The Role of Midwifery

'Midwifery is not all emergencies – although there is something of the unknown with every delivery. I remember being little more than a shaking wreck with the first baby I delivered – and I still find the adrenaline keeps pumping until the placenta is out – every time . . .'

Midwife Gill Watts

During the final year of a nurse's training, one of the decisions she or he usually makes is whether or not to go on immediately to qualify in midwifery. The thought of yet another examination daunts some. But for many Christian nurses, especially those who are praying that one day God may lead them to work overseas, midwifery is almost an essential.

Elizabeth, who trained as a nurse at Barts in London, is a good example. She had been a Christian since her teens and came from a Christian home. She had been considering for some time the possibility of working overseas. It appeared to her that midwifery might prove a vital qualification. She applied to do it in Bristol and was very pleased to find other Christian nurses on the course. Her training was interrupted, sadly, by the death of her father and she did her second six months in Newport, Gwent to be nearer her mother. 'It was a very good choice, as I was already thinking of applying to go abroad with VSO. I had to adapt from the very big modern hospital in Bristol to a much more basic maternity hospital in Newport.'

She also needed to learn how to speak the local South Wales dialect! She enjoyed her spell of training there enormously and thereafter was accepted to work overseas with VSO in Kenya. She found her midwifery was put to good use in various mission hospitals, though spiritually it was a hard time. Politically too Kenya was in turmoil, and to crown it, there was industrial action at the hospital and the volunteers were left to run the hospital.

On her return from Kenya she eventually managed to find a staff midwife's post at her old London hospital. 'It was billed as a temporary job – and I was still at the hospital twelve years later!' Problems arose from the fact she was suffering from culture shock in reverse. In Kenya she had been able to handle much more responsibility as a midwife than in her present situation. Overseas she had been delivering babies by forceps and back in London she felt she could not prescribe anything without asking a doctor's permission. Frustrated, this is largely why she moved on into gynaecology, though she would have even less responsibility than a midwife.

Most nurses who choose midwifery do so because they enjoy being part of the exciting drama of new birth and the joy and elation of the parents. Others call midwifery 'boring' and are reluctant to do it because they prefer to nurse sick people.

Patients in general wards have illnesses and medical problems for which individual assessment and planning of care is necessary. Pregnant women are usually in the peak of health and the Nursing Process fails to fit adequately into this area. So widely recognised is this that there is even some doubt whether the midwife should be called a nurse at all. The word 'nurse' implies illness, midwifery is concerned with health.

Midwives consider nursing to be the younger profession. As explained by one midwife tutor: 'The midwife has an honourable and ancient history – being mentioned in the Old Testament for instance.' Another basic difference between nurses and midwives is that the latter are practitioners in their own right – they are autonomous. They can make decisions in a similar way to a doctor, whilst a nurse cannot. For example, if a midwife is looking after a woman in labour and she wishes to give her an analgesic, she can do that without referring to anybody else. She can also administer pethidine, which is a controlled drug, when a nurse on her own cannot. Furthermore, the midwife can even decide whether or not to make an incision into the woman's perineum to deliver the baby, though this is a surgical operation. She can then suture the woman's perineum afterwards. The midwife can also admit and discharge mothers on her own authority.

There are changes afoot in the training of midwives. Previously only qualified nurses could do a midwifery course. Today there is an increasing number of schools of midwifery where an RGN certificate is not necessary. One benefit of the direct entry courses is that the student midwife will be less likely than a trained nurse to view the woman in the labour ward as ill.

Nonetheless, some midwife students – and practitioners – recall not boredom but the crises they faced when doing midwifery. For though it is not typical nursing, midwifery can make big demands on the midwife's or student's initiative, as Gill discovered in her first eighteen months doing midwifery in London. She found herself coping with several emergency situations and pleading: 'Why won't that wretched baby buck up and breathe?' 'Is this woman ever going to stop bleeding?' 'I can't get the placenta out! Oh no! It's stuck!' 'What on earth am I going to say to the parents of this stillborn baby?'

As a Christian midwife, Gill was glad to be able to pray in these difficult situations.

It is so good to know that we have an emergency line to heaven. Whether we are just observers or else caught up in the thick of the action, it always helps to be able to pray. But, then, midwifery is not all emergencies, although there is something of the unknown with every delivery, be it normal or otherwise. I remember being little more than a shaking wreck with the first baby I delivered. And forty-five deliveries later, I still find that my adrenaline keeps pumping round until the placenta is out and everything is checked. Only then is it really possible to relax and join in the elation of the parents. And yet, although the parents are usually bursting with gratitude to all the staff who have looked after them, I have never heard one spontaneous word of thanks to God for the gift of a baby. It is certainly a sad reflection on our humanistic society when Man becomes the object of praise and thanks and the Creator and Sustainer of life gets forgotten.

Unfortunately, there are also the occasional tragedies. Will someone explain why they always happen to the nicest people? Somehow the loss of a baby often seems to bring out the very best qualities in a couple. And when all the formalities are over, there is often nothing we can do but pray that one day God will bless them with a normal healthy child.

Something else that has disturbed me greatly is the large proportion of women who have had one or more terminations in the past, often without the knowledge of their present husband or partner. One can only guess at what emotional and psychological (not to mention physical) damage has occurred as a result. When we read in the Old Testament about people sacrificing their children to idols, it makes you wonder if we are much better. After all, is there really a lot of difference between practising infanticide on the one hand and abortion on demand on the other? Basically it seems to me it is only the idols that have changed.

Of course there are always the few terminations performed for valid reasons, such as gross abnormality of the fetus which is incompatible with life. I looked after one such lady, and I was very impressed by the courage of both herself and her husband especially as they had already lost one child with severe spina bifida. The most galling thing about the whole episode was hearing another woman deliver in the room next door. When given her baby to cuddle she was totally uninterested and could only complain that it was a girl and she had wanted a boy. My poor lady was grinding her teeth and saying 'I'd be grateful for either if only it was normal.'

Before I started the midwifery course, I can remember being asked at my interview 'Do you think you will mind being treated as a student again?' 'No of course not,' I replied. But as the course progressed, and I moved from ward to ward, it gradually dawned on me and my fellow students that a more appropriate question would have been, 'Do you mind being treated like a witless moron?' . . . However . . . there are many things about midwifery that I enjoy. It differs greatly from general nursing in being orientated towards good health instead of illness, and it certainly makes a change from doing dressings and giving pressure area care all day.

It is still true of course that many nurses view midwifery qualifications as a possible stepping stone to a greater goal. Some choose to qualify in midwifery in order to work in the community as a community midwife or health visitor. Others go on to take up a higher post such as sister on a general ward or a labour ward, or aim towards one of the very new neonatal units.

After a spell as a staff nurse in London, Hilary chose to do her midwifery at a smaller hospital in Manchester. There were only about sixty to seventy maternity beds and six midwifery students in her intake. Though the unit was small they had the advantage of seeing a good deal of their midwifery teachers. The course lasted twelve months then; it is eighteen months today. She found the experience really worthwhile. She loved midwifery and helping to deliver babies. She reckoned it was one of the most positive nursing experiences to be in and might have remained in it. But the staff in the unit were old-fashioned and set in their ways and did not seem to be good at handling the students or the mothers. Hilary decided to move on immediately to a medical ward as a senior staff nurse, soon to be promoted to junior sister.

None the less there are always many midwives who remain as such. If they choose to become midwife teachers they still have close contact with mothers and babies through their students. Christine is an example of this, having practised or taught midwifery in Britain and overseas for over eighteen years. She has many happy memories to recall amidst the hard work and busyness of her years on various labour wards.

She trained as a nurse originally in Harrogate in Yorkshire, and had already started to think about working overseas. As a young Christian nurse, she had met through her church and hospital fellowship a number of missionaries and Christians working for companies overseas. In 1969 she was accepted to do midwifery in Liverpool as she knew it had a high reputation. The Maternity Hospital introduced her to some likeable and voluble Irish Roman Catholic families. Her home by this time was on the other side of the Mersey in the Wirral.

One of the families from her church in Upton came home from Zambia and Christine was delighted to talk to them about their work. They had been instrumental in bringing her to a living faith of her own. Now they were suggesting she might apply for a vacancy as a company nurse in Zambia on a two year contract. In due time she was offered the post and flew out with her friends to take up her post in a small hospital in the Copper belt with a former missionary doctor in charge of midwifery.

He relied on the nursing and midwifery staff to do as much as we could on our own and we only called him in at the last minute if he was really needed. However, he suddenly remembered after some weeks that since I had trained in Liverpool I must know a certain type of breech delivery. And, of course, this particular lady we were tending was a breech presentation. Now normally in Britain, doctors would deliver breech births. But he asked me if I wanted to deliver this patient's baby. I did not like to admit that, though I had seen it done many times, I had never actually done one. I felt utterly terrified, but I took a deep breath, and said I could do it. He then left us to it and we coped – thank God.

Christine enjoyed the work, and the hot African sunshine. She also made some wonderful Christian friends as she was introduced to a number of the local churches and was entertained in many homes. She valued that hospitality highly, because she was far from home and family for the first time in her life.

She returned to the UK, took her City & Guilds Certificate in Liverpool and went on to become a midwife tutor. She found the course very demanding academically. 'I was sad still at the thought of moving out of practising midwifery which I had loved. Being a teacher meant a complete change of jobs even if I was still in the same hospital. At least we worked on the wards and we were part of the backup as we trained the students to deliver babies. I liked delivering babies, but there is much more to being a Midwife than that, and, as a tutor, I had to cover all of that. For instance, there is the antenatal care the woman needs for the nine months before the birth. Today we are concerned too even about preconceptual care.'

Some months after qualifying as a midwife teacher, Christine felt it was time for a move. She had grown out of the job in Liverpool. She had wondered if her next job would be in research, but when that did not materialise, she sought a challenge by joining the staff of one of the country's foremost maternity hospitals in London. The midwife teacher's post she managed to get certainly gave her scope to stretch herself and she had long wanted to live in London.

When she joined the staff in the mid-1970s, there were five other tutors with more experience than herself. She was faced with a new intake of ten midwifery students every three months. The course lasted a year. She was also included in selecting the next intake of students. Moreover she was having to teach subjects she had never tackled before and she was truly grateful for the support she found among her colleagues, some of whom were Christians.

As they selected each batch of new students and watched the last group qualify and leave the staff were being forced to face the awkward question as to why so many midwives qualify but do not go on to practise. The question is still being asked in Christine's more recent job in Leicester. Are the wrong students selected in the first place? If the wrong ones are selected where are the right ones? The question has great relevance because every country that cares about providing proper care for its mothers and new born infants needs plenty of good midwives.

Despite the frustration of losing so many midwives after they qualify, what makes it all worthwhile, Christine believes, is that greatest joy ultimately to be responsible for the safe delivery of a healthy baby.

This is very real and alive – to be dealing all the time with the birth of babies – and handling the babies too. A lot of the women in labour are usually young – the same age as the midwives and students. They are not old and frail like many of the patients on our general wards. The students enjoy being part of the lively maternity ward ethos that seems much more healthy in every sense of the word – and pregnancy itself is normal and natural. Few are ill in fact. Moreover, we are dealing with a process which most women on the whole would love to experience for themselves. They can easily identify with this and rejoice to be part of it.

6

Gynaecology and the Ethical Problems

'This area appears to be an ethical minefield: with abortion; the use and abuse of contraceptives, in vitro fertilisation, donor sperm, womb leasing and other methods to get round infertility . . .'
Senior Manager Elizabeth

There are many advantages in moving into gynaecology. Elizabeth, who spent a good deal of her nursing career as a sister of a gynaecology ward in a major London hospital, spoke of very varied types of medical care – and some truly rewarding relationships with her patients.

I have found over the years that the ups have always made up for the downs. What has kept me going was the tremendous sense of being involved in helping people recover – the joy of seeing them improve and go home. If they do not improve, there is joy in seeing patients facing whatever it is they are facing – sometimes that means helping people to come to terms with their own death; in other words, the fact that they are *not* going to get better. Several examples spring to mind – as a Christian sister of that ward. Several relationships were very precious. There was one woman of great courage. She had already lost one leg through a lymphoma. She was admitted to the Gynae ward because she had developed cancer of the vulva. We did the most mutilat-

ing operation on her. But we got her over it somehow
– with God's help. Then we had the most awful difficulty
helping her to pass urine because the urine would shoot
out an an odd angle and it excoriated her leg. Thus,
during her stay I was caring for her and I got to know
her very well.

When she went home, she would come back to see me
for special treatment. For about twenty months after
her operation she would drop in and see me whenever
she was in the out-patients clinic. Then she had to be
readmitted to my ward because she had gone downhill
greatly and had secondaries developing.

Unfortunately when she was readmitted to my ward –
and was obviously dying – I was on holiday helping at a
Scripture Union house party for two weeks. I arrived
back to the ward on the Monday to find the staff saying,
'Oh Sister, Miss P. has been readmitted and has been
asking for you every day.' Sadly, when I visited her
bedside, she was not conscious. We knew each other
well – and we had built up quite a relationship over the
years. So I sat down and held her hand saying, 'Oh Miss
P. I'm back, I've been on holiday. I've been away on a
Christian holiday. I'm so glad you are here so I can tell
you all about it . . .'

So I sat and chatted quietly to her all about it and what
good things had been happening at the SU camp. You
know, within half an hour of my arrival back on the
ward, she died. I know she had waited for me to return
and that I mattered to her. She knew I cared very
much about her and her needs. That was a very moving
experience.

Elizabeth spent five happy years as a sister of that gynae
ward. As a Christian she was glad to be able to stop the ward
routine to hold daily ward prayers. She stood in the centre
of the ward under an archway and read a prayer followed by
the Lord's Prayer, and even the Mrs Mopps would pause in
their cleaning to take part. It would normally follow the

Reports and everybody, doctors included, was asked to pause for those few moments. 'I wanted to make clear that we believed that God has his place on that ward – that we believed in prayer as well as in physical care.'

There were other wonderful examples of helping Christian patients and their families to come to terms with fatal illness and its implications. There were other Christian staff on the ward but, as sister, Elizabeth had the privilege of building up relationships. One young married woman, Jane, was admitted with ovarian cancer and she was one whose faith was sorely tested by her condition.

> We had put this lady in a side ward in isolation because her white corpuscle count was very low. Her treatment took the form of chemotherapy – and she was very dispirited. When we talked, part of her problem was that some well-meaning Christian had given her the impression that as a believer she had to die gloriously and she was feeling anything but glorious. I believe some Christians can be quite cruel in this way. So I was able to talk to her about her condition, because over the months she was in and out of my ward, especially towards the end. We talked about her actual dying. We talked too about the valley of the shadow of death. Even though we are Christians and know we are going to be with the Lord when we die, it is still a valley.

Elizabeth also made time to get to know Jane's husband and her young children who were facing such loss. After Jane had died, her husband wrote Elizabeth a wonderful letter which touched her deeply. 'He said that I had been a real help to her as well as to him. I was very thankful to God for opportunities like that.'

While Elizabeth was sister she came to know and work with a number of consultants and several chaplains. She could prove constantly the advantages of having such good relationships. Once she was put in a difficult position by a patient's question. Usually it is the doctors who disclose to patients the seriousness of their condition; in this instance the houseman appeared reluctant. The patient was obviously not going to live much longer. Just as Elizabeth was escorting the houseman along the beds, this patient woke up from her comatose state, looked Elizabeth straight in the eye and asked, 'Am I dying?' Elizabeth said something like, 'Well, it may not be very much longer now . . .' The doctor was furious. 'You have no business telling her like that,' he said. But Elizabeth defended herself by saying to him, 'I believe nothing would have been gained by evading the issue. She knows me and trusts me.' But that was only possible to do because she was also trusted by her consultants. Elizabeth would not recommend that other sisters should tell a patient they are dying except in rare circumstances.

Another responsibility which also landed on her desk as sister of a gynae ward was the care of a large number of women undergoing abortion. She confessed it had been quite a battle when she faced the full implications of abortion, but it became clear after considerable heart searching that she could not be a sister on that ward without being willing to look after terminations of pregnancy. She knew it would be unfair on the rest of the staff team. This is still her position today as she helps to recruit nurses and midwives for a big new gynaecology hospital in London. Only staff willing to assist with abortions will be employed there.

The whole area of this nursing specialism is in Elizabeth's own words 'an ethical minefield: with abortion; the use and abuse of contraceptives; in vitro fertilisation, donor sperm; womb leasing and other ways of getting round infertility in either spouse'. She recognised it was therefore not a simple area for Christian nurses and midwives to work in.

Among Christian student nurses and qualified staff there are many differing attitudes to nursing care in this area. Some would happily assist in terminations, others would not.

The Christian student nurses from St Thomas's Hospital were typical of many others. They had been given a leaflet about abortion care when they started their training. They were told about the conscience clause whereby they could opt out of working in this area if they chose. But that did not mean they could refuse to care for a woman who had been admitted for an abortion. In practice, there are all sorts of grey areas. One student who had worked on a gynae ward, having signed the conscience clause, was faced with having to do the pre-meds – the drugs that are needed to prepare the body for anaesthetic – for a woman having an abortion later that day. There was only one other member of staff on duty. 'I felt really unhappy about it and I said to the other girl: "Is there any way I can get out of doing this?" She said she could only hope that the night sister would be understanding and not make a fuss if the student refused.'

It is clear that this area proves difficult for Christians. One Catholic newspaper recently headlined a front page story: 'Catholic doctors shut out' over an article stating that 'Young Catholic doctors are being forced out of the fields of gynaecology, paediatrics and geriatrics because of their faith.' Nurses, too, who refuse to care for women having terminations on our labour wards or gynae wards, are being 'forced out' too and excluded from certain posts.

This is certainly true of the new Hospital for Women in London, according to the Christian senior manager. It would be impossible to become a permanent member of staff on a gynae ward there and not be prepared to look after termination patients. It would be similarly impossible to become a ward sister and refuse to care for abortion patients. She believed, as she had discovered for herself, that it is not fair on the rest of the staff team. This is not mere theory. In her own nursing career, Elizabeth had to work this through for herself. In her thinking and rethinking on this issue she reasoned that it was the doctor's or surgeon's decision to accept those abortion patients on to the ward – not even the sister's ultimately. It was wrong

then to refuse to care for these patients. She had been
struck, too, by a phrase she had read in John's Gospel
chapter 8 about Jesus and the woman taken in adultery.
Jesus said to her attackers 'If any one of you is without
sin, let him be the first to throw a stone at her.' The story
goes on: 'At this, those who heard began to go away one
at a time, the older ones first, until only Jesus was left, with
the woman standing there.' *(New International Version)*.
Elizabeth considered it significant that the oldest were the
first to slink away. She believed it was older people who
were less self-righteous about ethical problems such as
abortion, and not the youngsters who were quick to judge.
In her experience also, it was the older staff who were
ready to assist with abortion patients; it was the student
nurses who were more judgemental. And Jesus himself
said to that needy woman, 'Neither do I condemn you –
go and sin no more.'

In her role as sister of a gynae ward Elizabeth made
every effort to help these women. She tried hard to find
opportunities to talk to them when they were admitted to
her ward for a termination. She sought to ascertain if they
were happy and sure about their decision to have an
abortion and whether they really understood the full implications of what they were doing. Then she could support
them better in their decision.

'On one occasion I was taking this girl down to theatre,
myself accompanying the trolley. As we went up the ramp
into the theatre I said to her again "Are you sure you want
to go through with this?" "No," she said, "I've changed
my mind."' By this time they were in the anaesthetic room.
Elizabeth tried to delay the anaesthetic being administered, but got little cooperation from the anaesthetist. In
the end she asked the theatre porter if she could speak to
the consultant who was operating, and whom she knew.
She explained to him that the patient had changed her
mind and requested permission to take her back to the
ward. He agreed. She commented that if she had not been
a sister it might well have ended differently.

Elizabeth, like so many other nurses, can recall attending her first abortion. It was a gruelling experience. What shakes most nurses is the fact that the aborted fetus is perfectly formed. 'Horrendous!' is the reaction of other Christian nurses who have watched abortions being performed. If sisters or tutors are alert to the needs of their staff or their students then there may well be some kind of support offered, but often new nurses and students can be quite shattered by having to assist in theatre at terminations. Many nurses, sadly, seem to have no support when they are faced with disposing of an aborted fetus on their own.

Sister Esther, who trained in Cambridge, remembered her own sense of shock as a student nurse, when for the first time in theatre she had to take 'a little dead aborted baby to the sluice and wrap it up and throw it away. I found that extremely hard and it haunted me for weeks.' Looking back she felt very strongly that no student nurse should have had to do that alone. The sister could have arranged for another staff member to do it or be present. Today Esther attempts to support any of her staff or students who may be similarly devastated by this task.

Though most Christian nurses appear to loathe abortion and speak of it as a form of infanticide, it is not a neat black and white issue. It falls into the grey area of hating the sin while having compassion for the sinner. 'These abortion patients still need to be cared for, and as Christians we do not want to condemn the sinner instead of the sin,' said Sister Jane, working in a big London hospital. 'It is very easy to sound pious and say that we will have nothing to do with abortion. But that seems not a very Christian attitude. We need to see the human need, not the sin.'

Moreover, the major human need in these cases is not the attempts beforehand to counsel and ascertain that the termination is definitely what the woman wants. The primary need is for proper aftercare, when the patient returns from theatre. There is then a crying necessity for aftercare to help with the sense of loss, or guilt, or grief and this appears to be the time when care is often most lacking. One newly qualified staff nurse on an acute gynaecology ward in a London training hospital in the 1980s wrote thus:

The abortion debate, which over the years has enjoyed surges of publicity interspersed with periods of quiet, once again was in the news with MP David Alton's attempts to push through one of his Private Member's Bills. In Christian circles opinion has traditionally followed a one way street: termination of pregnancy is wrong as it constitutes the destruction of human life. The difficulties for the Christian nurse are those associated with their right to refuse to nurse such patients, and to avoid placements on gynaecology wards. However, the abortion business goes on relentlessly, providing a much demanded service as is demonstrated by the statistics: over 170,000 'therapeutic' abortions carried out in England and Wales in 1985.

Nursing women undergoing termination of pregnancy is a crucial task involving physical, psychological and spiritual care: a truly holistic approach. Women undergo this procedure for a variety of reasons, and in most cases it is a difficult decision clouded by guilt and mental trauma. The irresponsible image attributed to those girls who have abortion after abortion, and appear to use it as a means of contraception may be true only for a minority; but even then this may represent a sad reflection on society rather than on the girls themselves.

Women admitted for termination of pregnancy on the gynae ward where I worked were divided into two groups. First there was the conveyor belt style procession of suction terminations mostly between eight and twelve weeks, which formed a large proportion of every gynae list, and which were referred to lovingly by one ward sister as 'The Factory'. These were short-stay patients who came and went, often in secrecy, received a minimum of counselling and very little follow up. Shortages of staff and time meant that resources were frequently diverted to more acute, iller patients at the expense of these 'minor cases'.

The second group was regarded in a somewhat different light. Arrival of these patients was dreaded by the staff, talked about in whispers and usually engendered fraught discussion as to who was to be responsible for their care. These were women undergoing late terminations of pregnancy, for whom the procedure is lengthy and traumatic for both the patient and her carers.

It may be argued that one's ethical stance should be the same for both groups. If life begins at conception, then the act of therapeutic abortion constitutes the taking of that life, whatever its gestation. While by no means belittling the stress suffered by those undergoing suction terminations, it is however a fact that, in terms of physical and emotional trauma, there is some difference between a suction termination under general anaesthetic in very early pregnancy, involving the normal medical and nursing care for a minor operation, and the procedure for late termination which is described here.

Most women undergoing abortions in the UK do so for reasons under Clause 2 contained in the 1967 Abortion Act: 'the continuance of the pregnancy would involve risk of injury to the physical or mental health of the pregnant woman greater than if the pregnancy were terminated'. Some may see this as covering a multitude of sins and providing for 'social abortion' on demand. However, some of the late terminations I am referring to were part of the minority performed because of a known or suspected defect in the fetus.

The procedure used was as follows: an amniocentesis was performed and a mixture of Prostaglandin and urea injected into the amniotic sac. This ensured both death of the fetus and its eventual expulsion from the uterus. For the woman, this was the beginning of a painful and distasteful process which can last from a few to twenty-four hours and which carries certain physical risks, for example, haemorrhage and infection. The normal outcome was for the fetus to be delivered into a bedpan and removed to the sluice: the placenta sometimes delivered spontaneously but was frequently retained, necessitating dilation and curettage.

For the women, the ordeal was frightening and gave rise to feelings of guilt and disgust. They *never* seemed prepared by their clinics or by referring medical staff for the often long labour involved, or the fact that the fetus is fully formed at this stage. It was rare for a woman not to want to see the fetus and nearly all wanted to know the gender – but, in the case of a woman who did not wish to see it, this was quite difficult to achieve practically as the woman's cooperation was required at all stages.

For the nurse caring for her, the whole business was extremely stressful as medical staff were on another floor on the obstetric unit, and were often unwilling to attend an aborted fetus when other priorities called. It was, furthermore, a psychologically shocking sight for the nurses – it was known for nurses to feel ill and have to leave the room – when the fetus was delivered.

Probably because both nurse and patient were made so vulnerable, the situation made for a uniquely open relationship – and the time spent together provided for much discussion. The hospital took patients from a socially deprived inner city area and most of these women were in desperate circumstances. One girl's common-law husband had beaten her up and deserted her. She and her two small children were living in an overcrowded battered wives hostel, and the circumstances left no room for another child. Another girl's common-law husband was in prison, and she was expecting her second baby. She had a brother with muscular dystrophy and an amniocentesis had shown she was expecting a male child. Knowing all too well the problems of this dreadful disease she felt neither willing nor able to cope with such a handicapped child. A further complication was that her boyfriend's mother, a devout Catholic, had called her a 'baby killer' and told her she was condemned to hell. It takes little imagination to realise the guilt and private hell this woman was going through.

One seventeen year-old arrived, accompanied by her nineteen year-old sister, the only person she would name as next of kin. Early in pregnancy, she decided to keep the child but then at sixteen weeks, her boyfriend had left her. This girl became seriously ill as a result of complications and had to spend twenty-four hours in the Intensive Care Unit. Her parents were unaware even of the pregnancy – their shock and grief, had she died, does not bear thinking about.

A recurrent factor in discussions with these women was their tendency to talk about spiritual things – even in cases where they did not regard themselves as Christians or religious. A common thought was that the pain and guilt was a punishment from God: another was that God was condemning them or casting them out. In my experience, this group of patients has one of the greatest spiritual needs of all – and yet how many Christians are prepared to care for them?

Another sad fact is the disposal of the aborted fetuses. It may seem distasteful – but fetuses from both natural and induced abortions were delivered into bedpans and removed to the sluice. Eventually (usually several hours later) they were inspected by a doctor to assess whether or not the abortion was complete. After this the fetus was transferred to a kidney dish and a lid was placed over it. It was then collected by laboratory personnel for 'paediatric research'. The mother's consent was almost never sought for this, despite the fact that many women felt a sense of acute loss and were curious as to the fate of the little life they had felt obliged to part with.

This would seem to raise an important dilemma. Under the 1967 law a fetus under twenty-eight weeks gestation has no rights as a human being and is therefore just thrown away with no chance of any form of funeral or Christian service. In other words, a little perfectly formed human being lies floating in a pool of blood and urine for hours, and then is sent to be dissected like a rat. Feeble attempts were made by me to pray over these little bodies from time to time; but this must represent a tiny drop in the ocean.

Research by a woman's magazine and other media sources has unearthed some shocking facts about women who have abortions: about the lack of counselling, the emotional traumas involved and the psychological damage which can persist for years. It is a sadly neglected area of care where young girls admit themselves for a general anaesthetic procedure alone, unwilling to name a next of kin, and frequently leave hospital alone to go home on public transport, their only present from their care givers being a packet of contraceptive pills.

It could be said that it is the greatest failure on the part of the medical and nursing profession in general, and of those of Christian faith in particular. Moreover, I believe this could be attributed to a failure on the part of society as a whole, whose inadequate health care and social facilities are at least partly responsible for the status quo.

(Alison Lucas: *Pacemaker*, April 1988)

It must be said that many hospitals have provided more humane means of disposing of aborted fetuses, arranging for cremation in hospital and disposing of the ashes with reverence and respect. It must also be said that since that article was written, in April and May 1990 the Government passed a new Human Fertilisation and Embryology Bill allowing embryo research under specific conditions and shortened the permitted span for abortions to 24 weeks.

Experience on gynaecology wards leads some nurses to move on into the very new field of fertility research and care. There is no escape from the ethical dilemmas here. Revolutionary new techniques for overcoming infertility open up amazing possibilities to avoid barrenness. Sometimes the methods experimented with leave much to be desired. Christian doctors and nurses have had to exercise careful ethical judgment to make sure God-honouring standards are maintained.

One of the advantages of working as a clinic nurse say in a fertility clinic is the hours. Gone are the shifts and duty rosters that working on a ward entail. Clinic work is usually Monday to Friday, 9 a.m. to 5 p.m., and Staff Nurse Claire who was recently married fully appreciated having weekends and evenings at home. In the newly opened outpatients department in a big London hospital the fertility clinic operated alongside an expanded gynaecological clinic.

After a year in the clinic – and having had to move with it to the new building, she still loved the work. She relished the contact with the couples who came for help and enjoyed working for the gynaecologists and the obstetricians who were also consultants at the hospital. Some of these doctors had pioneered much of the research into, and setting up the programme of, in vitro fertilisation (IVF) at the hospital. This had been developing in leaps and bounds over the past six or seven years though the department had been in operation for much longer. The husband's sperm and an egg from the wife are put into a test tube to fertilise, then returned to the woman's fallopian tube for the baby to grow there. However, the success rate is not good – which Claire found disappointing.

The clinic operated like a small out-patients department and Claire was called Fertility Clinic Nurse. Not only did she work down in the clinic, she also went up on to the gynaecological wards if necessary and so had not lost all contact with the wards. She had mixed feelings, though, about no longer being on a ward full-time and missed the relationships with the patients and the staff team. She even missed the exercise of walking up and down the ward to care for the patients.

More to the point, when one of our patients in the clinic

feels really ill, I miss the speed of the ward when treating
patients. But it is still a caring role as a clinic nurse –
though we are caring in a different way. Instead of
bedside care, we are more like counsellors and advisers
– which is another kind of caring.

She also does physical examinations as they seek to elimin-
ate any reasons why a couple are infertile.

These people are grieved by their childlessness. So, as
you carry out the various physical examinations and tests
you are asking them questions – often painful questions.
I found often that such was their distress that I was
having to counsel and advise. It became an inevitable
part of the job . . .
   In distress people often turn to a nurse and pour out the
woes they might not tell others. That is when you end
up sitting and listening sometimes for hours. And I find
this counselling role challenging. Though a lot of it is
very personal and sexual too – so it can be quite demanding also. And you learn to be quite careful. You must
not thrust your views on the patient. You are really
meant to listen and offer advice – give information too
if such is available.

Here was the element of uncertainty about her work that
Claire had discovered as a Christian nurse. Having become
a Christian through her local church before she started
nursing, she met up with some excellent Christian friends
in her training in London. Since becoming a fertility
clinic nurse, parts of her work demanded great sensitivity
and delicacy. Personally she did not approve of all the
methods available today to overcome infertility. You find
quite a lot of conflict in your own mind over these
issues.

Take an example – at the hospital where I work, we do
not do any work with donor sperm. But, for some people

that is the only way they can have a baby. (We know they could adopt; but finding babies to adopt is nearly impossible these days.) So a lot of people opt for Artificial Insemination by Donor (AID). Now as a Christian I am not happy with that option. But I cannot deliberately refuse to give the couple a booklet about AID – because I have them in the drawer in the clinic. We have to discuss it as an option. I feel it is best to give the couple the leaflet and I can then tell them my feelings – which are – that AID is interfering with nature. To me it appears to be going too far – it seems to me to be almost like creating babies out of incest. It means the sperm is not your partner's sperm – and I do not think that is right.

However, many of my patients go ahead and have AID because they do not think it is wrong. And they feel it is better than adopting. Adopted babies are neither yours nor your husband's. At least with AID it is half your baby.

Claire worked mainly with the IVF cases, in fact. There was another nurse who was responsible for AID care, so Claire could pass on enquirers to her while stressing the seriousness of the step they were taking. Her mind was full of the problems that could arise when a baby born as a result of AID grows up. Who is its real father? Do you admit to the child when it grows up that he or she is half someone else's? For Claire AID seemed to pose more problems than it solved, and certainly more than adoption created.

It saddened her that some people felt so strongly about not being able to produce children that they became mentally ill. To her they had gone beyond the point of reason – they could not grasp that having a baby could bring a whole host of problems. In their desperation they forgot that.

Claire had learnt from experience how to deal with some very overwrought women. She had to be very careful what she said to them in case she might add to instead of relieve their pain and tension. At the weekly staff meetings they discussed each patient and their needs. 'If we feel someone needs extra care or attention, we have this pool of outside counsellors who step in if needed, especially qualified sexual counsellors to whom the patients can be referred.'

The one certain factor about the subject of infertility is that it is an area that is constantly changing. New techniques are constantly being discovered. In a recent book John Stott attempts to put the whole debate about abortion (and infertility techniques) into some perspective. In a chapter entitled 'The Abortion Dilemma' he ends by asking how the Christian concept of the uniqueness of each human fetus in God's sight might affect our thinking and action:

> To begin with it will change our attitudes. Since the life of the human foetus is a human life, with the potential of becoming a mature human being, we have to learn to think of mother and unborn child as two human beings at different stages of development. Doctors and nurses have to consider that they have two patients, not one, and must seek the well-being of both. Lawyers and politicians need to think similarly. As the United Nations Declaration of the Rights of the Child (1959) put it, the child needs 'special safeguards and care, including appropriate legal protection before as well as after birth.' Christians would wish to add 'extra care before birth'. For the Bible has much to say about God's concern for the defenceless, and the most defenceless of all people are unborn children. They are speechless to plead their own cause and helpless to protect their own life. So it is our responsibility to do for them what they cannot do for themselves.
>
> All Christians should therefore be able to agree that the human foetus is in principle inviolable.
>
> (John R. W. Scott, *Issues Facing Christians Today*, page 293. Marshalls, 1984)

7

Caring for Children and their Families

'Two or three weeks later they bring in this baby – fully
dressed and ready to go home – and I hardly recognise
the mother who is no longer distraught – or the baby
who is no longer at death's door . . .'

Sister Polly

The Nursing Process with its new emphasis on the patient
and his or her personal needs as central to the care plan
seems tailormade for the individual care of children. There
are currently two ways in which to qualify for this specialism – through doing a three year RGN course followed up
by further special training – or by doing one of the several
courses that lead to registration as a Registered Sick Children's Nurse.

Polly was one who was convinced from the very start
that she wanted to nurse children not adults. As she
explained:

This meant that I applied to do a special four year course
in Sheffield where you simultaneously study for an RGN
and RSCN, the equivalent qualification in paediatrics.
At the end of that it was made very clear if you failed
in either exams you failed in both before you became a
Registered Nurse in general and children's work.

I enjoyed paediatrics very much. It was all I'd hoped.

I'd looked at various other special courses but chose this 'mixed' course because it seemed to fit my needs best . . . During my grammar school years I had become a Christian partly through Crusaders . . . Then I went off to become a children's nurse in Sheffield because it had always been at the back of my mind. Because I come from a medical family and my mother had been a nurse, I was encouraged to proceed.

Polly pointed out one of the reasons why people choose not to nurse children.

Quite recently in Leicester where I have been a sister on a children's ward, I have seen that some learners who visit my ward discover that it is probably more difficult to cope with sick children because it is emotionally distressing some of the time. In fact some very young people have not got enough experience of life to handle these situations.

In the children's nurse training course that we did we had to get to know the normal first before we could learn how to treat the abnormal. How can one recognise a sick child if one does not know the normal child? Also, because of the new emphasis on care in the community they took us student nurses to visit children's playgroups, or we spent a week in a GP practice maternity unit, and also with some school nurses; we also saw some school health schemes for children in action.

My training took four and a half years in Sheffield. We were moved about a bit between the Children's Hospital, a separate 200-bedded place, and the hospital for adults nearby – where we started with a period of six months and had further spells later. Over 50 per cent of our time was spent at the Children's Hospital though.

I quite enjoyed all this transferring back and forth but after my first allocation of six to eight months of my first year with children (which I adored) I then did six to eight months of an adult ward and hated it!

What I actually enjoy about working on a children's ward is caring for the children *and* their families. Of course, today, parents are allowed to visit or stay and have much more say in the nursing of their own children. I remember when I had to have my tonsils removed when I was quite young, I would have been much happier if I could have had my Mum there with me.

Now, more recently, in the small High Dependency unit in Leicester, I have to relate to the five families linked with the five cots. It is not just mums and dads who need to visit, but brothers and sisters too. In Leicester which is multicultural and multiethnic, we must remember the importance of the extended family groups and not just the needs of the 'nuclear' family.

When she was training in Sheffield, Polly had problems finding Christian fellowship. She went home to Manchester for many of her weekends off so she realised it took far longer than it might have done to get involved with the local churches. She did try a large Anglican church but it was difficult to get to know people. She discovered Christians there from the hospital but they did not seem to recognise her out of uniform.

Having gone on to do midwifery in Leicester, Polly chose then to care for neonates. She liked the church she had then joined. It was smaller and friendlier and she was soon introduced to other Christians in the hospital and became a member of a weekly home group. She was aware that there were Christian nurses and teachers as well as paramedicals and a secretary from the School of Nursing in the congregation. This helped to make her feel much more settled when her work situation was not always easy. Eventually she became a staff nurse and soon a junior sister of a children's surgical ward of twenty to twenty-six beds for all ages.

As always I was a bit scared of the new responsibilities. When I was the one in charge, then I knew the buck stopped with me. I was frightened of the newness of that, and I was still unsure how much freedom I had to act alone or in consultation with others. By the time I moved to the high dependency unit I'd got over most of my problems of adapting to handling responsibility. In fact I was asked to open the new unit – and that produced its own problems. One of them was to get the staff to feel more responsible for what they did. It was all too easy for them to say 'Oh I'll leave that to Sister.' I tried to encourage them to think of ideas of their own and to share them with the other staff and then carry them through . . .

Once again I have come to appreciate my Christian friends, and that some of them understand the problems of hospitals and management matters. Despite all these problems and changes I would never give up nursing. For me there are still too many things about it which make it worthwhile . . . First you see a child and the very distressed parents; the child can quite literally be at death's door, when he or she is admitted. Then after a few days on the unit the child is moved on to one of the children's wards because he is improving. Great relief all round. Then, two or three weeks later, they bring in the child for me to see – fully dressed and ready to be discharged and go home. Usually I can hardly recognise the mother, who is no longer distraught. Moreover, I can hardly recognise the child.

One imagines that sick children find it harder than adults to cope with too many changes in ward staff, so it seems surprising to discover that part-time nursing happens on children's wards as it does on adults. The need for good long-term relationships with children and their families must still be counted as paramount. But, if the part-time children's nurses work always on the same ward or on night duty on the same ward, then continuity is provided.

Gill, who is married and has a growing child, was a member of a team of part-time trained children's nurses who form what is called a 'paediatric bank' to work on a special neonatal unit in Leicester. The hospital is desperate for staff with this specialised qualification. Neonatal Intensive Care is such a specialised new field that it requires nurses and midwives who have had that particular training. Being 'on the bank' means a nurse works the hours which suit her or him part-time. It is somewhat like being an agency nurse.

I have been a part-time sister on the neonatal unit for six years – it is a big unit of thirty-six beds and an Intensive Care Unit where the neonates are cared for. People say that two years of neonates is enough for them and I have been doing it for over six years! I really love it. It is extremely high-powered and demanding with a lot of sophisticated machinery in the ITU. There is always a lot of equipment to monitor. Preterm or sick babies are usually born on the labour ward – they are preterm if born earlier than 28 weeks and if they are in difficulties they are brought to us. In fact, if the baby shows any sign of life after a premature birth or even a termination, he has to be given a chance to live whatever the circumstances. The saddest problem is when the baby turns out to be severely disabled.

But at twenty-four to twenty-eight weeks babies are never the result of termination. They are born as a result of early labour, and the unit helps to save these babies born prematurely. It is great, because often the mother thinks there is no hope for her baby and there is. On the other hand, we still face those awful moments when the baby is obviously not going to live despite all the care we lavish upon him. Sometimes the fact that we have kept a baby alive for two to three days gives the parents time to get to know the little person and it makes it easier for them to hold the memory in their hearts. It is still heartbreaking for us all.

In those moments of pain and sadness I have found my Christian faith is a great help. Also we have two chap-

lains on call who will come and sit and talk and listen –
and pray with them. Parents may ask for the baby to be
baptised and he will do that too. Typical of the kind of
caring if the baby is very very sick and the parents are
not present – one of us will cuddle him so that he is
given some sense of human warmth and contact. This is
another way of 'specialing' a small babe. Sometimes,
sadly the mum never has the chance to cuddle these
little ones for themselves – they are born sick and have
to go straight onto a ventilator – even if the baby is
dying.

Over the years I have managed to cope a bit better
with the loss of these babies. It will never be easy to get
used to death, though maybe I am finding it less difficult
than I used to. But it is especially hard when a baby is
born at full term and falls ill as a result of abnormalities
or as a result of a difficult delivery.

Moving out of hospital, the variety of uses for a children's
nurse qualification is amazing.

On the community

An area where the care of young children tends to domi-
nate is health visiting. Many nurses prefer to take the
battle for better health from hospital-based care to the
community. District nursing and health visiting both cater
for patients who require care at home. The latter prides
itself on majoring in preventive care.

Jackie, now a district nurse, is married and has three
children. Having finished her RGN training at a London
hospital, she left nursing to raise a family. Eventually
she decided to work part-time in Public Health and was
attached to a health centre in North Kensington.

. . . it was very crowded with lots of tenement blocks
and many immigrant families. Nothing could shock me
I felt since I had not long before done three years as a

student nurse, then worked in casualty when I qualified. In fact I found I loved working in that area and my job provided quite a variety – I was called a clinic nurse to start with and then later I became a school nurse also. I was an inspector of school children's feet, eyes, teeth and hair – a 'nitty Nora' doing health checks! I loved doing that too and I did it for a couple of years as a combined clinic nurse and school nurse.

In the clinic I helped to weigh the babies and also to run two family planning sessions. Sometimes in the family planning sessions I found things a bit beyond me – but I knew I could always ask the advice of an older lady in the clinic who knew much more than I did. In term time, I was a school nurse, and in the holidays I assisted the health visitors with the visiting of the geriatric patients in their care.

Margaret got married during her final year of nurse training.

In due course, just as she was planning to train to become a health visitor, she became pregnant and decided instead to do a kind of 'child minding' job looking after the children of two local doctors. She had still intended to move on and train. 'But I stayed working with them instead. After I had had my own baby I went back to looking after theirs and mine – three very young children together – they were quite a handful!' The family subsequently moved and Margaret had her second child so she preferred to concentrate on bringing them up and did the occasional part-time job.

A very high proportion of nurses go on and qualify as health visitors partly because they then have responsibility for many small children. Usually health visitors have to do a separate training after gaining their RGN. Robert represents health visitors who do an integrated course. He took the four year Bachelor of Nursing course at Manchester which qualified him as a nurse and a health visitor. In fact he opted for the latter, once he had worked for some years in various hospitals. He is married with a family. Though he enjoyed his spell on paediatrics during his training, he felt at the end he preferred to work with well children rather than very sick children. 'Caring for sick children is a great art,' he says. 'I knew it was interesting to do from a medical viewpoint but I felt I was more interested in children as children, not patients.'

Recently he was seconded by his local health authority to work with the National Society for the Prevention of Cruelty to Children to work with the families of abused children. He accepted with some trepidation, conscious however that as a Christian he hoped God could use him.

He became a member of a multidisciplinary team working mainly with five social workers under a team leader. They exemplify the Government's new approach to child abuse entitled 'Working Together'. The whole initiative represents a new phase in the NSPCC's own development, too, as it seeks to set up child protection teams around the country to meet the huge need. The teams are experimenting with a variety of methods.

Some of Robert's more demanding roles include taking part with social workers and the police in investigations into alleged child abuse in families with young children and participating with a female social worker in a therapeutic group for adolescent girls. 'Of course, before I could do that it had to be established that the girls were happy for me to be there – a man – because the vast majority of sexual abuse is perpetrated by men.'

Usually, Robert emphasised, the victim is abused by a member of his or her own family and feeling under threat dares not speak about it. There is also a deep sense of letting the family down. This is an immensely complex area to respond to but as a Christian Robert has been struck by a number of important aspects. One of the main agonies is the feeling of guilt experienced by victims. 'They feel they should have stopped the abuser. It is their own fault it happened. That guilt is very destructive. It is vitally important to help the victim to see that this is a misplaced guilt feeling and they are not responsible for what happened. They must learn to forgive themselves.'

Accepting the fact intellectually is one thing, but the deep-seated feelings of anger and guilt have to be dealt with. If these can be stopped from turning inward, they can be directed at the person who was responsible – the abuser.

This is one aspect that I have had to wrestle with as a Christian. The fact that, within the therapeutic programme that we follow, we work towards helping the victims to shed the responsibility for their victimisation and place it on the abuser.

Yet, I recognised, to take that a stage further is immensely difficult; for the Gospel here challenges the victim, asking him or her to forgive the perpetrator which is far, far harder. I began to come to a beginning of an understanding of how to move forward on this when listening for the first time to a performance of Verdi's *Requiem*, especially the 'Dies Irae' – 'Day of anger, Day of Judgment' section where the frightening, harsh, vivid hammer blows on the huge bass drum seem terrifying – especially to a new listener. There was God's anger, it seemed to me, against sin represented by this fearful banging of the drum. I could identify that anger – that power of anger, with some of the anger I had seen unleashed by the victims of abuse. It helped me to know that God does care about what happened to them – that there is a judgment. We will all be judged – vengeance is mine, says the Lord.

Further, I know that the anger for what those men have done has been unleashed on Jesus Christ on the cross. Listening to that music gave me a whole new insight into the meaning of the crucifixion. It was only then it began to make sense. It enabled me to see there is a hope for these victims of abuse; not because those men were not responsible but because they too can be forgiven because the punishment has been taken. There is a way back to God and forgiveness for them.

One of the things that people of a humanistic frame of mind very often will not allow, is for people to experience true guilt. They make it just a guilt feeling with no real sense of moral responsibility. But then that denies the person true healing, true forgiveness. You can apply only therapy to a feeling, whereas you can heal guilt because there is forgiveness at the cross if the failure is repented of before God.

In his secondment Robert was finding much to learn. 'It is a very new area of expertise and we are all learning together. For instance, we are working with and seeking to understand the perpetrators of sexual abuse because they are people too. Why do they do these things? How can they best be helped? It is a controversial area and far too early to reach conclusions.'

However what has become clear is that many abusers have been victimised themselves, sometimes sexually, in their earlier years. 'It does not excuse what happened but it certainly can contribute to this pattern of behaviour. Those people need help also. But it is extremely hard for them to respond because it entails them having to accept responsibility for their own actions. Thus it is also hard to engage them in therapeutic programmes which might lead them to healing.'

Hospice care for children

Among the many varied types of paediatric care there is one final area that should not be forgotten. This particular field has grown in the past decade or so with the growth of the hospice movement and the recognition that there is a need for specialised care of the dying child as well as the dying adult. The name most associated with this development is Sister Frances Dominica who helped to found Helen House in Oxford. She has assessed the unique elements of this delicate area of nursing care. There are three demands for anyone who wants to nurse or care for dying children: the need for the carers to step back and allow the family to cope in their own way; the need to allow them to be the ones in control, not the nurses; and more important the need to take time to listen.

Most nurses who have had experience of this specialised type of care are amazed by the resilience and honesty of the children themselves and their acceptance of their prognoses. One such boy of twelve who died at Helen House in 1985 was quoted by Sister Frances Dominica:

Dying isn't really dying. It is just like opening an old door into a new room, coming from an old room into a new room, which is the place where you're going to live. Heaven, where you came from. Where you came from you have to go back to. That's your real home. I mean, we will have to go one day when it will be the happiest life of all. I mean this earth is very happy but there are riots and things. But when we go to the other life, no sickness, no pain, no tears, just full of happiness and joy. I'm looking forward to that day. Heaven is so beautiful, God can't describe it to us. We'll know when we get there. I'm glad really that Jesus kept it a secret, because it will give us a surprise – it will give us such a big surprise.

And when I die, I do believe that Christ will look after my family. I shall always look down on them if I go before them. I will be there in the midst of my family. They might not see me but I'll be there, watching them, looking after them all the time.

8

Theatre Work, Surgery and Intensive Care

'Working in the ITU with neonates was so stressful that
many staff did not stay for more than two years . . .'
Sister Gill of an ITU unit

Another highly specialised area of nursing is theatre nursing. There are nurses who do not mind that the patients
are anaesthetised and unconscious. They find stimulus in
this job, revelling in seeing an excellent surgical team
working in concert, from the brilliant surgeon and the
anaesthetist, to the theatre nurse who scrubs up and hands
out and counts the swabs. There are nurses who are thrilled
by seeing the latest surgical techniques and an operation
being performed successfully. There is excitement in being
a small part of that achievement.

But all theatre nurses complain of one aspect of the
work – the prolonged standing! Pat, who worked in theatre
for eighteen months, comments, 'There was too much
standing; after eighteen months I realised I was not really
enjoying scrubbing up. The other snag about working in
theatre is that it is very restrictive on relationships. You
only get to know the team you are on with – no one else
– when you are on duty. Then you are off home.' Because
there was no ward she believed there was no place in the
hospital to build wider relationships.

State Enrolled Nurse Kim, on the other hand, discovered as a student she loved working in theatre. 'It is nothing like what you expect – all blood and smells. You do not see a lot of blood at all. I worked in theatre for nine weeks; I enjoyed every minute of it – except the standing up all the time, all day long in one spot. I had to scrub up and hand the instruments to the surgical team. I can remember assisting at urology operations and terminations of pregnancy. I thought nothing of those then – and you cannot see much. But since I have become a Christian I feel differently.'

Having to assist at a termination can create problems for nurses who prefer to avoid this task if at all possible. Claire, who trained in London, found that when it came to doing her theatre stint as a student nurse there was a choice. 'The hospital was linked with a gynae hospital in Soho, but we were allowed to choose which theatre we would assist at and I chose to assist at the main hospital not the Soho one which did so many abortions. I felt I did not want to be so actively involved with abortions. Since then, I have cared for these patients, but usually when I was the only qualified nurse on the ward.'

Theatre work makes heavy demands in other ways also. Preparing patients for theatre on busy surgical wards when understaffed can prove to be too much for some nurses. Marilyn, a young sister of a surgical ward of forty beds, describes a typical day. Take reports from the night staff. Write in the daybook what jobs the nurses are to do. Do pre-meds for those going to theatre. See to bathings, dressings, drugs. If the other sister is on, leave her to sort out the office. Check that the patients for theatre are ready. Or do the pre-meds while the other sister does the notes for theatre. If there is a ward round, she has to talk to the senior consultant or the doctors and show them round and sort out any problems. If there is a nurse on her own she makes beds with her and chats to the patients as she works. She is able to be about the ward if the other sister is in the office answering the telephone and keeping up to date with the clerical work. 'Then I might go down to bring a patient back from theatre – each patient back from surgery would need quarter hourly observations, especially at first while unconscious. If you had six patients back from theatre in the morning and six in the afternoon, you had all those saline drips to monitor, blood pressures to take and pulses etc. Plus the admissions and discharges from the ward – that was why we were so busy.'

As a young Christian sister, Marilyn confesses she did not find it easy to join a local church when she was so busy – and she had been involved with a Christian fellowship in the hospital. She recommends to every Christian nurse the advantages of belonging to a supportive group of mature local Christians who can help nurses to find some way of praying through the pressure. It is wrong, she feels, to meet only with other nurses and not link up with the nearby churches.

It would appear that the crucial requirement for staff on surgical wards and in theatre is the ability to work in harmony together. The element of smooth team work can be highly rewarding – the staff on the wards preparing the patient for theatre and receiving them back afterwards, confident that the theatre staff have done their best.

Intensive care

Another highly demanding area in nursing is working in intensive care. So many revolutionary techniques have been discovered for providing life support that this forms a specialism all of its own, ranging from neonates to renal dialysis and heart patient care. Again, the nurse is not in the typical ward situation, but often working one to one with the patient.

In one hospital intensive therapy unit where neonates are cared for, the sister on the unit of thirty-six beds spoke of having usually one highly qualified staff to each patient. But the sister confessed that the work was so stressful that many staff only stayed on the unit for two years or less. As a sister, if she ran into any major problems she knew she could telephone for advice from another more experienced sister. 'The work here is highly pressurised and demands great concentration. In ITU there is always a lot of new and sophisticated equipment to watch and the staff cannot relax.'

Many patients come into ITU from major road accidents and often do not survive. This has a further impact on the members of staff who are so closely involved in that one to one relationship.

Patricia describes her reaction to this particular form of stress in a major hospital's ITU. She worked from September 1985 in an extremely busy eight-bed unit with a six-bed coronary care unit staffed by the same complement of nursing staff.

The patients on the unit came from all aspects of surgery, though mainly cardiac and road traffic accident patients, especially those with head injuries. We also took any medical patients who required mechanical ventilation and also some paediatrics, essentially those with neurological and respiratory difficulties. As you see, we had a wide variety of patients and lots of potential for sadness, loss and stress amongst both relatives and staff.

It became increasingly apparent to me that the staff were either unable, or sadly often unwilling, to learn what to say and how to respond to the tragedies we witnessed on a day to day basis. The staff had no real support structure either to work through their questions, frustrations or feelings of inadequacy.

I discovered later that many told their husbands or boyfriends and friends how they felt, but were often not understood so withdrew into silence. There was also not the freedom or the atmosphere on the unit for us to be honest enough to express our feelings to each other.

Meg Bond puts this beautifully. 'The role of the nurse consists of the expectation of her behaviour and qualities held by those around her and her own expectations of

herself. A nurse is often expected to be the solid ideal-
ised parent figure, the rock upon which those around
her can base their stability (rather than them finding
their own stability within themselves). Nurses often report that when they allow themselves to crumble a little,
they are met with expressions of surprise, dismay or
even contempt from their colleagues, family or friends.
'They also have within themselves feelings of failure,
from not having lived up to their own ideal image of
perfection. Whether we create expectations in other
people by setting ourselves up to be seen as able to cope
with anything, or whether we internalise these ideals
because of other people's expectations is rather like the
which came first – the chicken or the egg debate.'

After working in this environment for about a year the
Lord began to sow seeds in my mind about taking
some practical steps to alleviate some of these stresses –
because I'd already, in an informal way, become 'a
shoulder for people to cry on'. These feelings were
heightened when we had a particularly hard situation of
an eighteen year-old lad involved in a road traffic accident whose facial injuries were nothing short of horrific.
He was on the unit for two days before brain scan tests
proved to be negative and he was declared dead –
thereafter his organs were used for transplantation.

This lad's death affected me in a way very few others
have. I found I was constantly visualising him in my
mind and thinking about the trauma his parents must
have experienced and be experiencing. A week or so
later I mentioned casually how I was feeling to one of
the other nurses who had looked after him and she
almost hugged me saying that she was having nightmares
and was finding her feelings extremely hard to handle.
We talked about how we both felt at the time and over
the past few days, and it was a real release for both of
us, not least to find that someone else felt exactly the
same way and did not think us to be stupid.

God used this incident to convince me that I needed to

take some action. After discussion with some of my friends on and off the unit I felt it best to establish exactly how people felt and what they thought would help them best. So I devised a very basic questionnaire which gave people the opportunity to express themselves anonymously.

There were some revealing responses to my questions about how people felt about the stressful and difficult situations on the unit:

'Often I go home feeling confused and upset about a situation and not knowing how anybody else is feeling therefore I am left in a state of uncertainty.'

'It is easier to go home and forget about it than it is to talk about these stressful situations for some people – but is this good?'

'Great awareness and sensitivity of people's problems is very important.'

'It is important we are aware of how we all feel after say the death of a child, especially for staff who have been personally involved. Not everyone can go home and forget it.'

It seemed that I was the person on the staff who was willing to take some action by taking the responsibility for running a discussion group – with the guidance and help of one of the nurse managers who was also a counsellor for CRUSE. So the meetings began. But despite the initial enthusiasm only a few attended, but we were able to be open and honest with each other and share our fears of being misunderstood on the unit. I felt the Lord gave us some good open times and gave me the commitment and boldness to lead them.

Since that group began meeting, Patricia has moved on to another hospital. She heard, however, that the support group was still meeting occasionally through the initiative of another Christian nurse and the hospital chaplain too had become involved. She concludes:

The whole experience demonstrated to me anew the
need that we as nurses have to be listened to, taken
seriously and understood, and that nurses in highly
pressured situations need to have an outlet to express
their emotions. We may be seen to 'cope' but this is not
true and can be extremely damaging to us as people and
to our professional relationship as nurses. We need to
be allowed to be real to ourselves and to one another.
I'm convinced that in learning to understand ourselves
we become more effective in supporting each other and
therefore will be better equipped to give help, comfort
and support to both patients and relatives.

Talking to Christian nurses and student nurses at St Thomas's Hospital in London gave further insight into different
nurses' reactions to the pressures of ITU. One was a staff
nurse on a urology ward – a surgical ward – who had done the
hospital's post registration course in intensive care. There
were advantages as well as disadvantages in working in that
area, she felt. All the patients were unconscious – usually
asleep when she worked. 'On the renal ward too the patients
are not wide awake and demanding! If you do not mind
missing out on the more usual ward work of hands on caring,
then intensive care may be the place to be.'

Rachel on the other hand really enjoyed theatre and
working in the recovery room because the patients were
under anaesthetic and not too demanding. 'I am fine when
the patients are very sick and totally dependent on us, as
in a renal ward and after surgery. In fact I prefer to be an
acute nurse, working in intensive care. Yes, it is pressurised, but you don't usually do it long term. Normally in
ITU you work with one patient. In our unit there are
twelve patients but there are also twelve nurses on each
shift. You have to do constant observations to make sure
the patient is recovering from the surgery and the anaesthetic, especially when they are unconscious.'

Another student nurse in that group had worked on a
cardiac thoracic ward (where heart surgery is performed).

She had in particular built up a good relationship with one woman patient who was in the ward for a long time awaiting a major operation. Over the weeks beforehand they chatted and shared things.

I felt we had quite a rapport – and so, the day she was going for the operation we talked again. I could see she was really keyed up about it when I went to give her her pre-med. I was just about to give her the injection when she started saying, 'I am so frightened! I think I am going to die . . .'

She seemed genuinely scared that she was not going to come through that major surgery and she then added, 'Can you help me? Who can help me?' As a Christian I wanted to speak immediately to her and help her, but at that moment, there was another nurse nearby, so I did not want to talk to her about spiritual things in front of the other girl. I prayed silently that we might be left alone, so we could talk. I asked the Lord – if you want me to help this lady then make the other nurse move off down the ward.

Even when the other nurse moved away there were still other interruptions. But she asked me again, 'Can you help me?' We were alone at that point, so I asked her 'Do you believe in God?' She said, 'Yes I do.' I responded, 'Well why don't you pray to him for help in your special need of comfort and reassurance?' So she said she would. Of course I prayed for her too. When she came back from theatre, she was really much calmer. She told me she had prayed and asked God to help her. She said she had felt a special warmth around her as she went down to theatre and on her return.

What was tremendous was – that we had an even better relationship after that and over the three weeks she was in the ward I was able to chat with her about God's special care for her. When we had a special open Christian Union meeting in the hospital she accepted my invitation to come. She was much better by then in any case – and she listened to the speaker and had a long and fruitful conversation with one of the Christian hospital staff also afterwards.

In Australia, surgical techniques similar to the ones pioneered in Britain have made amazing changes to the care of heart patients. Again this is a stressful area as the success rate alas is not high. The patients are usually in the ward for a lengthy period, as has already been mentioned, and require highly committed nursing care.

Barbara, who trained as an RGN in Melbourne, stayed on as a staff nurse to work in the four-bed intensive care unit responsible for the care of patients having open heart surgery, which was very new back in the 1960s.

I found it a very demanding job as a newly qualified nurse. Part of the job was to get to know the patients pre-op and prepare them for surgery so that when they returned from theatre we were not strangers to them.

This meant you got to know the patients quite well. Because we were the receiving centre for the whole state of Victoria and Tasmania. We had patients therefore who were in hospital for quite long periods of time – far from home in some instances. It might take weeks and weeks of special preparation sometimes – so they could feel fairly lonely. This was an area of special need that as a Christian nurse I tried to respond to.

Barbara became a Christian before she started her nursing career. 'I had always wanted to be a nurse since I was knee high to a grasshopper.' She went straight from school into hospital to train. Thus she was fairly young to have to cope emotionally and spiritually with all the challenges of that open heart surgery unit. In point of fact it was her experiences on that ward which alerted her to the lack of spiritual care for these patients, and how she herself felt totally at a loss lived in her memory as a spur to action. She claimed she almost felt unable to cope.

As a new staff nurse I found myself working in a more senior position than I felt I was qualified for. For example, there was this young married lady from Tasmania, far from her home and her loved ones. She was staying with us and being prepared for open heart surgery – a double valve replacement, which was a pretty major operation though relatively safe. She went down to theatre, but when she came back to the ward, they had struck more problems than they had expected. She returned to us in an extremely low condition. During the course of the evening when I was caring for her post op doing the observations etc, it was awful. She had something like five cardiac arrests.

That was not unusual, but what was very unusual was her consciousness, the clarity of that consciousness between the first three arrests. She had tubes out of every hole in her body and others we had had to make to keep her alive. She was only in her thirties – it was very hard . . .

What made it harder still was that her husband and adopted son had come over to be with her on the day of the operation. During those three arrests, when I was caring for her, she could not speak because she was on a respirator. Yet she managed to convey, to communicate to me non-verbally that she wanted more from us. I felt quite helpless to know what to do apart from all the physical things that I had been doing. It seemed almost embarrassing – I knew she wanted something more than that, and this awareness created an acute sense of helplessness in me.

Then, after the fifth arrest, when she could not be revived again, I remember that same sense of helplessness flooding me again once she had died. As I tried to comfort the husband and the stepson I still had that terrible feeling that I should have done more. It was not just as a Christian I felt helpless but also as a human being.

I drove them back to their hotel in Melbourne in my car

– as one attempt at helping them but again felt totally
at a loss. What do you say to a man and a child who
have just lost their nearest and dearest? How do you
give them comfort? I felt deeply the painfulness of
their position – staying in a strange city and not knowing
anyone. I remember I felt that acutely. It seemed awful.

I think God used that experience to do some major
personal reviewing as I relived the whole situation again
and again. I went over what care was needed and what
care had been offered that lady. I realised that we had
been so busy trying to keep her alive that we had failed
to help in her dying. I thought, if this is all that nursing
is I'm not sure that is what I understood it to be. Surely
there must be something more? That set me on a long,
long search for some kind of meaning – and some
answers to those big questions like: What did it mean to
be a Christian nurse in those circumstances? What did
it mean to be a caring person? What did it mean to face
death?

I felt very strongly about that young wife and her pleading for something more – and my own sense of failure
in not giving it to her. I realised how inadequate as a
nurse I was – and as a Christian.

Barbara knew that as a Christian she could go off duty and
meet with her Christian nurse colleagues in the Nurses
Christian Fellowship group. She was deeply involved in
that from the start of her nursing career. But sadly, it
seemed to her then that her Christian life was encapsulated
in one circle and her nursing career in another. 'Many
times, on duty I felt I did not know what to say or do as a
Christian. And it is often thus in intensive care – you
usually do not have the time or the opportunity to call a
chaplain or anyone else.'

There were four beds in that critical care unit and she
remembered that it had been very demanding even with
two patients let alone four. Over the many years since
that experience Barbara has never forgotten her sense of

failure. She had recognised that Christians do not have a monopoly on love and caring. 'But I think we often fail because we do not put our faith into practice. So I set myself the goal – to try and help myself and other nurses to put their faith into action in an integrated way.'

9

Psychiatric Care and its Related Fields

> 'Hands-on caring is less important than seeing if a variety of approaches can help them – you attempt to get to know them as people . . .'
>
> *Sister Beverley*

Most general nursing students only have to do a few weeks in psychiatry. Many Christian nurses understandably find psychiatric nursing disconcerting. Some in their placements experience unpredictable behaviour and even violence.

Jamaican-born Win, a student general nurse, was one who found her eight weeks in psychiatry difficult. She was working on a ward of a big longstay mental hospital. She had felt fairly apprehensive beforehand and her worst fears were realised. On her first day a patient tried to smash the window of the charge nurse's office. In the dining room another patient deliberately broke some glasses. Then within her first four weeks, an elderly man was attacked by a younger man with a broken cup and blood was everywhere. Win was on duty and had to try to clear it up. Fortunately her tutor arrived to rescue her. In fact, Win settled down after that and when she prepared and wrote up a special project on her psychiatric placement, it was highly commended.

Another area that Christian nurses find difficult is the

spiritual aspect. Some do not know how to act responsibly, sometimes through ignorance. As a student nurse, Charles had to learn this the hard way. Having become a Christian before he came into nursing he trained in Cambridge. As a fairly new Christian, he wanted to make his mark – and he still does. He began by wearing a tiny cross on his uniform lapel. He hoped that useful conversations and questions might result. He has found it exciting as many people do ask questions about what he believes.

When he was doing his RGN training he had some problems adjusting after public school, but otherwise he felt that nursing appeared to be a question of common sense and that even the boring bits had relevance! But as a Christian student nurse there were occasions when he found his beliefs and actions caused difficulties. On his eight week psychiatric placement he ran up against 'great inner conflicts, partly because of my Christian convictions'.

> Once qualified and looking back, I realise I was not right. You see, on that ward it seemed to me there was a tremendous sense of apathy towards the patients; no attempts were made to improve their lot by the staff. Some of these improvements appeared to me to be pretty basic – and if they were not caring for them physically properly, leaving them in a physical mess – that was wrong. You can't care for their mental sickness if you don't improve their physical wellbeing. In fact, I was not alone in those feelings. Others among the RGN students felt the same. It was more a case of what they were not doing that was wrong. There also seemed to be very rigid and dogmatic opinions about the treatment being given.

Charles was not popular for challenging the status quo.

There are however great rewards in being a psychiatric nurse. That was the testimony of Beverley, who found psychiatry suited her much better than general nursing where she had had an unfortunate and unhappy time. She resigned from her general training but spent a year working as an auxiliary while she applied to become a registered mental nurse. She feared she might have problems being accepted, but she found a place in a big London mental hospital.

There were similar placements around various wards as in her general training. The hospital was vast and old-fashioned with an enormous psycho-geriatric unit catering for some 800 to 900 patients. Another part of the hospital contained an addiction unit where alcoholics or drug addicts were helped.

Beverley maintained that this new training was definitely right for her. She discovered she really loved being a psychiatric nurse. There was less of the hierarchical system she had so disliked as a general student, she was called by her Christian name, the nurses did not wear uniform and the atmosphere was much more relaxed, especially once she had qualified. As a member of a multidisciplinary team of doctors, social workers, psychologists, nurses etc., even her humble opinions were welcomed and valued at case conferences. Building relationships with the patients and their families took on a new significance. She thought that by getting to know each one to the best of her ability, she was benefiting them. At the staff meetings everyone had a chance to air their views; when one shift handed over to another there were opportunities to report on any patients who needed careful observation.

However there were things she did not care for, such as staff shortages which she found 'demoralising and hard to cope with'. She discovered in her most recent post in the Midlands that the ward where she had started as senior staff nurse/acting sister had good staffing levels when she arrived. But it had gone downhill as many of the staff left. As she pointed out, in psychiatry if you have too few nurses and too many acute patients then it becomes dangerous and there is no continuity of care. This made her feel frustrated and frightened. Severely depressed patients for example do need supervision – with too few staff they may find their way out of the hospital and endanger themselves in some way – possibly by trying to commit suicide.

A surprising aspect of the psychiatric ward in the Midlands

was the number of her patients who were Christians. As with other kinds of nursing this can be a thrill – 'we have about six at present in various states of depression who have such a low opinion of themselves some of them might well be prepared to harm themselves.' In her understanding she felt they particularly needed to sense the love of the Lord, so she prayed with them seeking as a Christian to support them. She knew their families too and prayed for them as well. Off duty as well she had them on her prayer list – and her church was also happy to pray for them as long as confidentiality was maintained. Here was the added element of care a charismatic Christian sister could give to this job. Historically the churches and psychiatry have been at odds. It is good to record that those days appear to be past.

Churches also need to learn about the needs of this huge area of medicine, to prevent ignorance and fear continuing to scare Christians off becoming involved either in psychiatric nursing or in aftercare organised by bodies such as the Richmond Fellowship, MIND or the National Schizophrenia Fellowship. Mental illness comes to more families than physical illness so this represents a prime area of need that challenges every Christian.

Beverley had always maintained that the Nursing Process was ideal for psychiatric nursing, for it was an area where patients were really treated as individual people. 'We do not put the patients into medical/psychiatric boxes labelled manic depressive, schizophrenic, psychotic or whatever. We try to see them as human beings. Hands-on caring is less important than seeing if a variety of approaches can help them. You attempt to get to know them as people, and in order to do that your own personality may well be important too.'

On psychiatric wards it is usual for patients to be out of bed and dressed. There is often a rota for cleaning the ward as it is not used for aseptic surgical techniques. If necessary, of course, a psychiatric nurse would wear gloves and an apron. But it is more common for any patient requiring surgery to be transferred to another ward or another hospital.

On a psychiatric day ward, the normal pattern would be

for the patients to eat breakfast and then to receive their medication. Some would be booked for electroconvulsive therapy, others might have an appointment with the psychiatrist or the psychologist or another member of the team. The majority of them would probably go down to occupational therapy. Others might stay in a group situation on the ward. Group therapy was a popular means of moving patients on in their slow, slow progress back to feeling normal.

Recalling her own training Beverley remembers a six week introductory block of lectures in the School of Nursing. They learnt about the Nursing Process and the basics needed for all nursing such as anatomy, physiology and basic psychology. Then they looked at the nursing care of the mentally ill and various forms of the illness itself. Another invaluable section looked at how to communicate – verbally and non-verbally – with mentally or emotionally disturbed patients. Depressed patients become withdrawn and find it extremely hard to talk.

Beverley did not find her placement on the psycho-geriatric wards easy as it was distressing to see confused minds in healthy bodies. Sadly too visitors could go unrecognised. Some patients also appeared totally unaware of what the staff were seeking to do for them. But there was still great care shown on that ward with staff seeking to improve their physical condition and maintain their dignity whatever their mental state. Occasionally there were examples of charge nurses abusing and mistreating their confused patients who could not answer back. The reason might be that the more dynamic staff prefer the more dramatic acute admissions wards or drug dependency units and leave the longstay geriatric wards to staff who have little interest in their patients or in improving anything in case it creates extra work. The result is that those patients remain completely institutionalised.

Many hospitals, however, have rehabilitation wards which aim to assist elderly patients and others to recover their self-confidence slowly over a period of time before, hopefully, being discharged into the community. They are helped to learn how to go shopping again and how to budget and acquire some of the social skills they may have lost during their stay in hospital. But for some the hospital has become their only place of security and they do not want to leave.

If they are extremely fortunate the local community will help discharged patients adapt with drop-in centres or hostels and homes run by the local Health Authority or charitable bodies. Local churches should be vital caring centres if they could only bring themselves to rise to this challenge and provide a relaxed, unstructured place for ex-patients to drop in. But it is public knowledge that the continuing closure of Britain's longstay mental hospitals has not been met by a corresponding opening up of community care for ex-patients. One aspect of the multidisciplinary care of a patient includes the work of community psychiatric nurses – who are partly looking for ways in which they can move more patients out into the local community. Their other function is to support mentally sick patients who are already living there and seek to prevent them from having to be admitted to hospital. A major report published in 1989 called 'Dream or Nightmare?' by the Quaker Board for Social Responsibility and Education makes it clear that many many more community psychiatric nurses are needed as well as local initiatives to help provide community care. In God's goodness, perhaps that report may stir up greater concern for this gaping hole in the Government's plans to close more and more longstay mental hospitals.

Sometimes the local community can provide vital resources for patient rehabilitation such as art classes or music therapy sessions. The hospital at which Beverley trained has had the services of such gifted people for many years.

Community psychiatric nurses (CPNs) were being trained alongside her. She moved out into the community herself in the second year of her RMN course. The students were attached to the local Community Mental Health resource centre and worked with a CPN assisting with group therapy sessions, seeking to help those referred by local GPs or psychotherapists and the nurses. There they worked with people who suffered from various phobias or accompanied the CPN on home visits – helping with patients who were counselled at home, or had requested treatment at home. Sometimes they visited some of the ex-patients who were then living in a smaller local health authority community home.

On many occasions they administered injections of the newly developed long acting drugs, enabling many more people to live outside the hospital by helping to prevent them becoming disturbed or disinhibited.

Another form of care which Beverley saw at first hand was helping addicts to kick the habit, whether drugs or alcohol. This form of self-abuse has so many complex causes it proved an extremely tough area of her work. Addicts dried out in the detoxification ward then underwent five weeks of group therapy to help them avoid relapsing. Much later Beverley worked for a country-based organisation that ran a hostel and community centre to help drug addicts.

Beverley did not enjoy her placement on the therapeutic community ward in the hospital. That was where people with serious personality disorders were treated, some possibly undergoing group therapy or psychoanalysis. In her final year she was based on a longstay ward and discovered she much preferred the shortstay acute wards where the pace was faster, with people coming in extremely ill and going out again later seemingly much better.

I found that was rewarding and interesting. Though at times stressful, it usually proved worthwhile. However, in all my training, if I was faced by a tough time or a tough personality, I reminded myself that I believed God wanted me there in that kind of nursing. That helped me to hang on through some rough spots. Though the work can often be gruelling and though some patients are very hard to cope with, I would not do anything else. I love the contact with needy people and seeking to build relationships with them and seeing them respond slowly; say, one patient is depressed and has almost lost the will to live – it is a joy to see them later gradually coming through to enjoying life.

The hardest part was the fact that so many patients came back into hospital within a few months of being sent home.

Beverley enjoyed being able to give of herself to the patients she tried to assist. But the danger could be that they became overdependent, or that she and the other staff were being manipulated by them.

After qualifying Beverley stayed on as a staff nurse on a twenty-four bed female acute ward where she had worked as a student and had liked the sister. But all too soon it seemed she was left in charge and finding the pressure fairly tough, though she learnt how to run a ward on her own. To her the frustrating thing was she had to spend far too long in the office coordinating things, speaking to relatives and answering the telephone or talking to doctors or social workers.

Her next job was at another London hospital as a staff nurse on a twenty-bed acute research unit. It was in a big general teaching hospital with a good deal more money to spend than her previous post. It was consequently better staffed. There could be as many as twelve staff nurses on a shift. The professor of the unit was researching into various therapies for psychiatric illness, in particular seeking to ascertain why some people became seasonally depressed in the winter months and giving them a kind of light therapy.

When Beverley moved to Coventry she became senior staff nurse then acting sister of a twenty-five bed mixed acute ward. However, staffing problems proved to be a major hurdle when six trained staff were reduced to four and three of those were totally new to the ward. So she had to spend precious time inducting them.

Beverley believes that with the fullness of the Holy Spirit in her life, and supported by her church and Christian nurse friends, she still has a great deal to give. She repeats that Christian nurses are greatly needed in all branches of psychiatric nursing. Personally she feels the need to seek the Lord's help and discernment, especially with spiritism and witchcraft on the increase, she finds her patients have been dabbling in occult practices.

Mental handicap

Mental handicap is another area of nursing that provides rich rewards. The new name for this is care for people with learning disabilities. A senior nurse manager who is a registered mental health nurse explains:

> The philosophy behind this new approach to mental handicap is that people who have learning disabilities have the same rights as anyone else to education, further training, proper ordinary housing, health services, economic security, a decent standard of living, to perform productive and useful work and have access to proper legal representation. Additionally they have the right to any special services that may be able to meet their needs, whether physical or psychological.
>
> These are people first and handicapped second. They are not children unless chronologically so. They have a right to be respected and valued in any community. Their disability only becomes a handicap when society is unable or unwilling to meet their needs.
>
> They are a heterogeneous group – some mildly learning-disabled people can function with minimal help and counselling in ordinary community settings. Others will have more severe difficulties and will always require help and guidance. Some will have profound disabilities perhaps including associated conditions such as severe spasticity, epilepsy, chronic physical conditions or heart or respiratory disorders, and some will present challenging behaviour. All are individual people in their own right with individual choices, preferences and needs just like anyone else.

Attitudes towards people with learning disabilities are often shaped by the terminology used, for example, before the Mental Health Act 1959 legal terms included now unacceptable words such as 'cretin', 'idiot', 'imbecile'. This act referred to 'subnormals'. The 1983 Mental Health Act opted for the term 'mentally handicapped'. This is the most widely used term in the United Kingdom.

Most mentally handicapped people live at home with their natural families as the carers. However, often there comes a time, even with support from community services such as members of the Community Mental Handicap Team, when either the family can no longer cope, or the person expresses the wish to fly from the nest. Several agencies can then be involved in the future day and residential care of mentally handicapped people. The statutory agencies are the local authority's Social Services department and the local health authority's Mental Handicap Services. Normally, the former tend to cater for mildly learning-disabled people who do not demonstrate a need for health care in the traditional sense. Less able people, especially those with chronic physical disability or illness or with multiple pathologies are usually catered for by health services.

A much larger number of people who do not live at home are cared for by voluntary agencies such as Mencap, United Response (Lantern Houses) and L'Arche. The last two are originally and broadly Christian based, as are David Potter's ACORN Houses (A Cause for Concern).

It is not necessary usually to have any formal qualification to be a senior care giver in most non-statutory services. However, social services require carers in a senior capacity to have a social work certificate such as CQSW or CSS. Health authority services require their prime carers to possess a certificate such as a Registered Nurse for the Mentally Handicapped (RNMH) although, pragmatically, they will sometimes employ RGNs, RMNs or RSCNs, as the specialist training does not keep up with demand from service areas.

The RNMH course is open to any caring person who

meets the usual nurse entry requirements. It is of the same length and status as other parts of the register held by the UKCC. However, although it will soon share a common foundation programme under UKCC Project 2000 proposals, it offers a rather different specialist core based on the fact that most people with mental handicaps are not actually sick. They are not 'suffering' from physical or mental illnesses even though some may have one or other of these as secondary conditions. Primarily the course is concerned with the total care and wellbeing of people whose ability to learn ordinary daily living skills is impaired, either due to some genetic condition (such as Down's syndrome) or because their neuro-logical system is damaged through trauma or infection (as in some breech births or in rubella syndrome) or because they appear to have a lesser intellectual capacity through unknown causes (idiopathic mental retardation).

Students learn how to assess and plan, implement and evaluate programmes of care tailored to the individual needs of the clients, just as their colleagues on general and psychi-atric courses. The emphasis, however, is very much on a multidisciplinary approach as no one specialist can provide all the required services. The nurse specialist will often be the coordinator of such a professional group as he or she will be the person best placed to understand the client's needs and wants.

The future of residential care is in the community in specially and adequately staffed domestic scale, small group homes. This in itself presents an exciting challenge to staff committed to the principles of normalisation and an ordinary lifestyle for their clients. Other nurses will find the challenge in being a full and valued member of a multidisciplinary Community Mental Handicap Team where occupational therapists, speech therapists, psychologists, psychiatrists, physiotherapists, nurses, social workers and others work together.

The term 'nurse' is only very loosely applicable in the care of the majority of mentally handicapped people. The nurse for the mentally handicapped is actually constantly called upon to be counsellor, advocate, befriender, defender, communicator, coordinator and provider.

Many who decide to apply for this branch of nursing have often worked as care assistants and feel they would like more say in how services should cater for the needs of clients. Hence a great many entrants are mature students who can bring to the service a wealth of personal experience, commitment and understanding often not found in school leavers.

A Christian nurse has unique help in carrying out duties and responsibilities which are often frustrating and disillusioning. The duty of the Christian nurse in caring for people with moderate or severe learning disabilities is basically to provide an environment whereby each person will appreciate warmth and love shown by those charged with their care. Christian nurses can, with tact, talk about the things that Jesus did on earth and the parables He taught. It is clear He always sought to teach the least able.

10

Terminal Care

'St Christopher's is about living as well as dying . . .'
Shirley du Boulay in her book about Dr Cicely Saunders

Death used to be the great taboo, especially in hospitals
where it was considered a total failure on the part of the
doctors and nurses. Today, thank God, that is no longer
true. The words 'quality of life' and 'quality of death' have
taken on new significance and occur more frequently in
nursing. Death is no longer treated as the enemy.

For all Christian nurses, especially, death is not the
enemy. The Christian has a special quality – a hope of
eternal life beyond the grave for all who trust Jesus Christ
for their salvation.

The phrase 'quality of life' has become very important,
often used as a yardstick for giving or withholding care:
What quality of life will the spina bifida baby have when
it is born? Should a termination of pregnancy follow when
the results of the scan have revealed an abnormal fetus?
Do we switch off the life-support machine keeping alive
the elderly patient who has no hope of recovery? Does
one give renal dialysis to a ninety-seven-year-old when
many younger patients desperately need it? Should a
course of antibiotics be administered to a frail elderly
lady with pneumonia who will remain hospitalised and

incapacitated with a slim likelihood of recovery and with no one to care for her properly at home?

These issues are what constitute many a case conference on the wards of Britain's hospitals. It is no longer the case that doctors decide alone, say, to switch off the life-support machine. Today the relatives and the multidisciplinary staff team will be asked to give advice about a patient as well as the nurses who have been closest to that patient.

Over the past twenty years, with the pioneering work of Dr Cicely Saunders at St Christopher's Hospice and the subsequent growth of the modern hospice movement, the term 'quality of life' has found a new meaning in the field of terminal care. 'Unless the body is reasonably comfortable, it is hard for people to be open to the spiritual comfort or the possibility of the peaceful death that Cicely Saunders longs for them to achieve. St Christopher's sets out to establish and maintain the highest medical standards with a firm scientific basis . . . The aim of the hospice is not to cure.' (Shirley du Boulay, *Cicely Saunders*, page 172. Hodder & Stoughton)

One of the major battles won by Dr Saunders was not treating death as a failure. In her work at St Christopher's, she has helped to prove that death is nothing to be afraid of. Before, dying patients were shoved on to side wards and not allowed to face up to their own death openly and with dignity. Now, in most hospitals, special courses are available for doctors and nurses on terminal care. It has become a standard part of their training.

Those who have studied this specialism speak of the new openness they can have towards the dying patient. However, there still is the vexed question of who should tell a patient his or her diagnosis and whether they should be told at all. Often the patient's relatives ask for the information to be withheld. In most hospitals it is normal practice for the doctors to tell the patients. But, many nurses have had to face up to the unexpected question quietly asked when no doctor is in sight. Often the nurse has to think hard then gently tell the truth.

Sarah became a sister at the hospital where she trained and gained one of the first degrees in nursing, a BSc (Hons). Her new ward was a male medical ward of twenty-five beds.

There were terminally ill patients some of whom did not know their diagnosis. When least expected she might be asked to tell them the truth. She knew it was the doctor's responsibility but over the months she began to discover that the consultant could not bring himself to stop at the end of those patients' beds and talk to them at any length. He would always walk past with a nod and a smile but avoided talking to them.

> I decided to pause at the end of their beds and ask him a few questions or suggest that he talked to them himself. The first time we moved along the ward and reached one of these very ill men I said to the consultant, 'Would you like to ask Mr S how the pain killers are?' The consultant looked a bit shocked, but I knew he was too much of a gentleman to refuse. He said, 'Sister, what do you want me to ask Mr S about?' And I told him. Eventually and tentatively, he began to take the initiative and talk to them. We used in the last few months I spent on that ward to break the bad news about their fatal condition to them together – which was much much better.

Later, Sarah was to fulfil a long cherished ambition to study terminal care properly by doing one day a week during her MSc course at Manchester University. She then helped to nurse the patients who were in St Anne's Hospice. She also did research on student nurses and their attitude to the care of the dying.

And much later still, having been a nursing process coordinator in Hackney, East London, she became nursing officer for the medical unit to Hackney Hospital. Finally she moved into local Health Authority management as an assistant to the chief nursing adviser in Bloomsbury. Her

many years as a member of NCF and a Christian who had
reached the top echelons of the profession were then put
to excellent use by the Fellowship. She became involved
especially with ethical issues as a member of their Professional Developments working group, in particular in
providing a Christian critique of the British Medical Association's 1988 Report on Euthanasia.

Terminal care has become a popular specialism and
Christian nurses find it a particularly challenging area to
work in.

Do these nurses view death with any special fear or
have experiences that draw them to face up to the full
implications of dying? Sarah, already mentioned, said she
had no fear about death because of her own experience
as a child. Her grandfather, who was a minister, lived
with her parents. He trusted and knew God personally. He
died when Sarah was aged seven. She recalled, 'He died
in his bed in my home and I knew that he had gone to
be with God – it seemed perfectly natural – he had gone to
heaven.'

Win, who came into nursing late in her thirties, believed
God had called her into that career and had later led her
on to make terminal care her particular specialism. As a
young Christian in her teens, Win had been baptised at a
small Pentecostal church in West London. It was the illness
of the pastor of that fellowship that made her think that
God's plan for her was nursing. As a close friend of the
pastor's family she became willingly involved in helping to
care for him. 'It was then that I discovered that I could do
things for him that I did not know I could do, and it seemed
to come naturally, this nursing instinct. For I had never
been in hospital and had chosen other ways of making a
career. The more I found I was able to do for him, the
more he seemed to benefit from my help. I started to
wonder if God was telling me that I was meant to be a
nurse.'

After she had qualified a close male friend aged thirty-
three developed cancer and was admitted to the hospice

attached to her hospital. Amidst her distress and grief at
his condition she realised that God might be calling her to
enter that challenging area and as a result she applied later
to do the hospital course in terminal care. She believed
this was a very vital part of her development as a person,
as a nurse and as a Christian sister. She felt a deep sense
of loss on the death of her friend, but was glad that his
death had opened up for her a new avenue of Christian
service.

The control of pain was one of the major steps forward
in hospice care. Esther is ward sister of a large London
teaching hospital, and has to deal with many terminal
cases. 'As long as it was a good death – that may be a
better way to help that person and their family. Of course,
this decision is taken only after discussion as a staff team
and we explain to the family. One thing I learnt from Dr
Saunders [she had worked at St Christopher's Hospice for
two years] was that the quality of life was more important
than the length of it.'

In her present post she finds it hardest when she and her
team of staff have to make these decisions without the help
of the relatives. She knows they have to be professionally
accountable. This is a heavy responsibility – knowing that
as a nurse she has the ability to give and withhold life. She
agonises over these questions and prays them through. 'As
a Christian, however, I believe that if God does not want
that person to die – if we withhold the antibiotics – they
will live anyway if God wills it.

'In other words, I rely on God's overruling power in this
difficult situation. I believe that a man is immortal until
his work is done. There is a tremendous reassurance that
there is a Sovereign God in the heavens and he is in control
– that is a great strength. I pray often for great wisdom
over these painful questions that we face.'

Furthermore Esther believes there is the special care
and support to be offered to the family of a patient who is
close to death. Very gentle, sometimes silent – it might
not be the moment for words. She might spend half an

hour sitting with them quietly because there is little more as a nurse she can do. She knows as far as possible that the patient is comfortable. Then there might be tears shed – there might not. Maybe twenty minutes or half an hour might elapse. Afterwards the family will say 'Oh Sister, thank you, thank you for all that you did . . . You've been marvellous.'

And Esther comments – 'I felt I'd done nothing. What had I done? Except to be there with them alongside them as a silent support. I had not walked away as their loved one died.'

In one of her recent experiences the patients were Christians – Ivy and Marjorie. They were best friends and lived not far from the hospital where Esther worked. Ivy was admitted first to her ward. She was in her mid-seventies and she had carcinoma of the pancreas. 'We knew she was not going to live. But she came from the same kind of Free Church which I belong to and as a Christian, she brought her Bible and hymn book into hospital.' So Esther made a point of making friends and grew to love both Ivy and her friend. Ivy's condition got progressively worse and by that stage their friendship had developed sufficiently to allow Esther to visit their home near the hospital. When Ivy was discharged Marjorie took up the burden of care and Esther took to dropping in when she could. But, after six months and as she grew worse Ivy was moved into Trinity Hospice where she died while Esther and Marjorie were with her.

After the funeral Esther still tried to keep in touch with Marjorie. Then Marjorie herself developed cancer of the bowel and was admitted to Esther's ward. She had a colostomy and made excellent progress although she was eighty. It was at that point that God was at work in her heart and she began to ask Esther many questions about spiritual matters.

Joy followed when she asked to be baptised, having made her peace with God. With Esther's help she was baptised and also joined the local church, a further source of great joy. It also showed the advantage gained by really getting to know the families and the home circumstances behind each dying patient.

Quality of life is of central importance in the care of the elderly. Take the experience of Jane who trained in a big London hospital. As a student nurse, she was sent to care for some geriatric patients in another hospital. They were on a rather run-down, longstay ward and the students' presence was not welcomed by the older permanent staff. The ward was in a grim workhouse-like building which added to its problems. The nursing staff had been there for many years working in the same old regimented way. To Jane it seemed 'absolutely awful!' The patients were not properly cared for, yet there was no readiness to alter and improve matters.

They were all fairly new student nurses so their training hospital decided they must have a tutor with them, if only to provide moral support. She remained with them the whole time to supervise the improvements their own hospital wanted to set in motion on the care of that ward. The tutor found it as devastating as the students.

Nor was there anything they could do quickly. Everything had to be done diplomatically and slowly. The patients were usually washed in the morning, they sat in their chairs until after lunch and were put back to bed again. Tuesdays and Fridays, come rain or shine, by rote they had either a suppository or an enema, whether they needed them or not. The long days were not brightened by many visitors sadly; they seemed doomed to be permanently institutionalised.

Most of the patients could not speak due to senility or the effects of a stroke. It took weeks of gentle persuasion to begin to make changes but eventually nursing care did improve as the students demonstrated.

Senior District Nurse Margaret who had worked latterly in the community before going on to manage one district, recalls with anger how she felt while nursing elderly patients. In one highly regimented ward for example the sister insisted that every woman patient wore a bow in her hair, whether she wanted to or not.

On the other hand SEN Kim working in Leicester grew to enjoy her care of the elderly ward. At first she admitted it was difficult. But the acute patients who were admitted did not stay very long. Usually after a month or so, they got better and were discharged. If they improved but could not go home, they were moved to a longstay ward and given intense rehabilitation. There were new ways of helping them to achieve this – physiotherapy, occupational therapy – for most of them had lost the full use of their faculties through strokes or falls etc.

Edith trained in Durham, doing a four year RGN course combined with orthopaedics. Much later, she trained as a health visitor and then became a field work teacher. She was confronted most strongly with ethical problems when she was caring for the elderly. Many of her orthopaedic patients were elderly people who had fallen and fractured a femur or had TB hip or spine. It was a very slow painful road to recovery. Many of the patients spent months on traction because they did not have some of the speedier modern treatments of today. Plastic hips were unheard of. She too found the wards were regimented and felt there seemed to be a lack of dignity too often in the way patients were handled. Once she became a sister on an orthopaedic ward herself, she was able to use much of this experience and seek to make changes.

She had responsibility for a female orthopaedic ward with forty beds in several different bays. The ward had recently been upgraded and she was determined to improve the nursing care as well. Imagine her first Christmas on that ward, a new sister trying her hardest to make something special of it. To make it more memorable, Edith asked her mother to knit some pretty bedjackets as Christmas gifts for the few old ladies who were in over Christmas. Then, on an icy Christmas Eve, her ward received eight or nine late admissions with broken limbs. Panic stations ensued at Edith's home where the whole

family were employed knitting bedjackets late into the
night! They were a great success – and one way of making
an impact on her first Christmas in charge of that ward –
showing practical love in action.

Ansley who had worked with the elderly on a rehabilitation unit in Coventry recalls:

> I believe there is something special about elderly people.
> They know they have lived their three score years and
> ten, and still have time ahead. One's elderly patients
> not only want to get better but also to get the most
> out of their remaining and very precious days.
> A relationship of mutual trust and understanding is
> built up on a rehabilitation ward for elderly patients
> who are recovering from strokes. Staff and patients
> together work out a programme of redeveloping the
> skills that were once a normal part of their daily
> life and taken for granted. These duties include such
> mundane small details as getting dressed, being able
> to comb the back of one's hair or making a cup of
> tea. Both staff and patient are subject to discourage-
> ments and setbacks which they need to work through
> together.
>
> Nursing staff new to the ward need seven to ten days to
> adapt to the patient's slower pace. Much more difficult,
> the newcomer needs to develop that special ability to be
> able to allow a patient to struggle with doing up his own
> buttons, resisting the temptation to do it for him, but at
> the same time to encourage him to complete the task in
> hand, by talking him through the process and afterwards,
> to give him a real sense of achievement.
>
> Each patient presents a new situation to the staff, which
> allows for new ideas, some more unconventional than
> others. For example how to hide a catheter bag when a
> female patient could not tolerate it by her leg. This
> introduced the idea of sewing a pocket to the inside of
> her skirt into which the catheter bag could be inserted.
> Not every idea we try works, and staff and patients need

to learn to laugh together at their failures. This helps to build up that 'special' relationship. Our relationships too do not end with the patient alone. Family help and support is always welcomed (and often very much appreciated in these times of staff shortages). Helping nursing staff with basic tasks instils confidence in the relatives and often helps them to feel more able to cope when 'Mother' is ready to return home . . .

Keeping in touch with the outside community is essential, and an extended part of any unit for the elderly is the programme of social activities, ranging from bingo to trips out in the summer. An elderly gentleman told me that since he had come into hospital he had learnt to play bingo, but his problem was that he kept winning pairs of socks he did not need!

With staff under pressure and money in short supply it would be easier to let social activities slip away, but I believe they are an essential part of the patient's rehabilitation programme. I also find that there are still many people willing to give voluntary help on my unit, and so nurses are able to concentrate on the skilled tasks. Added to this, it is therapy in itself to have new faces around visiting the ward to chat and help redevelop social skills and confidence often lost by a person having recently suffered a stroke or similar illness.

Rehabilitation has its sad times, just like any other form of nursing, but somehow the sadness is shared by relatives and staff and comfort is found within that sharing. Cyril was only sixty-seven years old when he came to us after his stroke. He quickly developed many skills but was never able to master dressing himself independently. Walking was a constant effort, although he did manage to walk with the aid of a stick, caliper and his wife. After six months we decided Cyril was ready to venture out and so we began the process of graduating from a drive out in the car to several weekends at home. After another two months it was decided that Cyril could go home and we would monitor his progress as he attended our day hospital three days a week.

On the morning that Cyril went home there wasn't a dry eye on the ward. Cyril and his family were crying for joy and the nurses and physiotherapists really didn't know whether they were happy or sad. Cyril continued to make excellent progress, but it was only a few weeks later, while he was walking out in his beloved, and much missed garden, that he suffered another stroke and died. Questions filled our mind – should we have discharged him earlier to give him longer with his family? Was it right that we insisted he was able to balance correctly, or should we have settled for a wheelchair?

As was our pattern, when the ward team was experiencing difficulties, we set an hour apart and talked it all through. We had made what appeared to be the right decisions in the light of information available at the time, and I reminded the staff of the time he was able to spend with his family and of the lovely way he had died in his own garden. Some days later a group of us went to Cyril's funeral – as we always do when we lose a patient – they are part of our family and we have become a part of theirs.

Working in a rehabilitation area one cannot work in isolation . . . It is a link in a chain and part of a much wider speciality. Most patients are referred from an acute medical ward for the elderly, or from the day hospital, or following a consultant's home visit or a GP's or district nurse's request. It is therefore essential that the rehabilitation nurse works closely with the acute ward nurses and day hospital staff, so that she is able to provide good on-going patient care. Rehabilitation work involves a great deal of trust: firstly to inspire confidence in a patient likely to become depressed, demoralised and in danger of losing his dignity; then to have the confidence to allow him to develop his own skills and independence by standing back.

I often wonder if Jesus felt the same way as I do when

patients go out when he sent out the twelve disciples 'as sheep among wolves' (Luke 10). He certainly experienced that same inner thrill when they returned: 'At that time Jesus was filled by the joy of the Holy Spirit and said, Father Lord of Heaven and earth! I thank you because you have shown to the unlearned what you have hidden from the wise and learned. Yes, Father, this is how you wanted it to happen.'

This chapter ends with a moving poem that was read by Thora Hird on the BBC1 Television programme *Praise Be*!

Nursing the elderly

He was a child before we were born
Now he is helpless, old and forlorn
He was a husband long years ago
He walked with his wife, their cheeks all aglow
His wife was a mother; she had babes at her breast
Caring for others and giving her best
He was a man, salute him for this . . .
Now he is withered and harder to kiss
Speak to him gently and nurse him with pride
Now as he waits to sail with the tide
Ours are the last hands he'll ever hold
Let him know love, now he is old.

(Written by SEN Kathy Doyle when she was working with the Chelsea Pensioners.)

11

Nursing AIDS Patients

'There is no doubt among those working in this field that the advent of HIV infection represents an uniquely sinister threat to the human race . . .'
Robert J. Pratt, Head of Charing Cross Hospital School of Nursing

The threat created by the upsurge of AIDS (Acquired Immune Deficiency Syndrome) has presented Britain's medical and nursing professions with one of its greatest tests this century. According to a report by Robert J. Pratt, Head of the School of Nursing at Charing Cross Hospital, HIV, the newly introduced virus which may or may not lead to full-blown AIDS 'is transmitted by blood and other body fluids in the following ways: 1 Recipients of infected donor blood and blood products; 2 Recipients of donor tissues, organs or semen from donors infected with HIV; 3 Inoculation of infected blood by contaminated needles; 4 Infants in the womb being infected by mothers infected with HIV.'

Robert Pratt continues:

Infection with HIV produces three possible outcomes: reflected thus: 1 20 to 30 per cent of infected individuals will develop full AIDS . . . 2 Another 20 to 30 per cent will develop a lesser form of illness known as ARC –

the AIDS related complex; 3 Approximately 50 per cent of individuals will not have symptoms, at least in the short term. All individuals infected, whether they have symptoms or not, will remain infected and infectious for life.

Two aspects of this condition indicate that HIV infection now poses the most serious threat to the public health since World War II. One, the numbers of individuals infected are enormous and continue to increase at an exponential rate, doubling every ten months or so. As we entered 1987, over 700 individuals in the United Kingdom had developed AIDS. By 1988 at least 2,000 cases will be seen in the United Kingdom (by the end of 1986 over 35,000 individuals in the USA had been diagnosed as having AIDS and in five years, this number is expected to increase to 235,000).

For every patient with AIDS there will be at least as many as five individuals who develop ARC. Some of these will progress to fully expressed AIDS. The number of individuals infected who are currently asymptomatic are staggering. In the United States estimates vary between 500,000 to 1.5 million and in the United Kingdom, the most conservative estimate is at least 30,000. These numbers are not static and continue to increase dramatically (at least 100 individuals in the UK a day are now being infected with HIV).

Health care workers are not at risk of acquiring this infection as a result of treating or nursing patients with HIV infection if they follow the sane and sensible guidelines currently being promoted by the RCN and other expert professional bodies. Draconian infection control procedures are not necessary and these patients can be nursed with complete safety in the community or in any hospital.

However, patients with this condition are at risk of mishandling by health care workers. This is often due to fear, ignorance and a lack of competence and confidence by those entrusted with caring for these patients. The moral and ethical issues raised by this condition are critical. All health care workers have a professional responsibility to remain clinically up to date.

With the vast numbers of individuals now infected, and the staggering projections for the immediate future, it is inconceivable that any nurse or other health care worker will not be caring for these patients. These young people are wide awake in their own worst nightmare and Christian compassion demands that they be cared for competently, confidentially and not be abandoned by those dedicated to caring for the sick. Prejudice and judgmental attitudes have no part to play in caring for any of our patients, including patients with HIV infection. Like our predecessors facing the great epidemics of centuries long past, nurses – and especially Christian nurses – must be brave in the face of this current threat to humanity, and arm themselves with knowledge, compassion and a rededication to all of the noble attributes associated with the great professions of nursing and medicine.

This includes a loving concern without bias, for those most at need. The Christian nurse is strategically placed to confront the calamity of AIDS and to make a real impact on the quality of care required by these patients.

The decision to move into AIDS care needs to be very carefully thought through. It is no light matter, and not everyone's family or friends are necessarily happy about it.

Heather became a Christian when she was fifteen and subsequently trained as a nurse when she left school in Leeds. She discovered her family were not altogether pleased to be told she was hoping as a ward sister to help to establish the first purpose-built NHS ward for AIDS patients in Britain. She has a good relationship with her widowed mother and her sisters who are all teachers. 'I felt it was very important to share with them my intention to take up this post working with AIDS patients. Initially they were very unhappy at the thought of me accepting that particular sister's post.' In the end, Heather's family have come to some kind of acceptance, and she was encouraged that they were putting her in God's hands in prayer as she applied for and eventually began her new job in London.

It proved quite a difficult assignment and she needed their prayer support. There was a great deal of hard work ahead. The new AIDS ward was formerly the hospital's isolation unit – now upgraded. The new twenty-bed purpose-built ward was opened in 1989 by HRH the Princess of Wales at St Mary's Paddington. Before that, Heather and her staff had months of unsettling and difficult adjustments to make working out how best to use the new facilities and have them ready for their first patients. It is the second AIDS ward in that hospital. Because of the infectious nature of HIV the ward has to be capable of preventing the transmission of the disease.

The weeks as a new sister were spent attempting to prepare her ward and her staff for the opening. Many were totally new to the hospital, which also demanded her time in helping them settle in; others were suffering from a sense of deprivation, having moved from better equipped wards elsewhere in the same hospital. She had to keep explaining that once the ward was fully operational, many of those problems would disappear. A sense of insecurity made some of the new staff concentrate all their expectations on the new ward, which was still not fully functioning.

The staff team are all qualified nurses, though at a later stage the hospital intends to train students there. Until then they meet with AIDS sufferers on the general wards. The team consists of one sister (Heather) and seven staff nurses. They rotate shifts and all do night duty. They have agency nurses to help as well. For a twenty-bed ward Heather hopes to have six staff on an early shift and five on a late, with three on night duty. Of the staff nurses, there is one senior staff nurse and then D and E grade staff nurses. The staff nurses are helped by one SEN and an auxiliary.

Two old wards have been combined to form one brand new unit with sixteen single rooms and two doubles. There are also twelve beds in the high dependency area for very ill patients requiring special care. It is all colourfully and tastefully decorated and very well equipped. Each room has its own TV, refrigerator, sink, shower and wc, cupboards and units – these were provided by a large donation from one of the AIDS charities, Crisis Trust.

Despite some early hiccups, Heather finds it a very enjoyable area to work in and personally challenging. Having worked earlier in her career in oncology, there are some similarities – the patients need long-term care and often the same patients are readmitted. However, running an AIDS ward provides extra tension, largely because she has had to face up to her own presuppositions and reactions to homosexuality. 'Your whole approach to these patients can be coloured by your own feelings about such people. In fact, our patients want to keep control of their lives while they are in hospital. They want to know what is happening to them and want a say in what things will happen to them in the future. This is known as self-directed care.'

Another delicate area she finds is the fact that not all of them know their diagnosis. Unless the patient makes it clear he or she does not want to know, Heather feels it is right to tell them. She bases this partly on her experiences at the Royal Marsden where the majority of the patients knew they had cancer and appeared not to lose out by it.

Then there is the vexed question of confidentiality. It is assumed that all the patients on her ward are assured of complete confidentiality with members of their own family or their friends. The staff are trained carefully to know that the details of a patient's diagnosis are not to be divulged to anyone. The press has been known to telephone the ward asking if a certain person has been admitted.

It is a difficult ward to manage. With its individual rooms, even finding her staff proves difficult sometimes. Communication was poor at first especially as there was no proper intercom functioning – in an emergency you just ran!

To seek to overcome these snags and to help her staff work better as a team – she tries arranging a meeting for them all to attend. But that is also difficult with up to twenty on the multidisciplinary team, and that number will rise once the home care team is started. Moreover she hopes to establish a support group to help all the staff in what might well be quite a stressful area of medicine. There will be an outside counsellor available to discuss privately problems in relationships and other frictions as well as the deep sense of bereavement caused by the death of one of the patients. 'I believe it is very important that these things are brought out into the open and discussed with someone who is able to be objective and detached.'

Since she began the job, it has become clear to Heather that some of her staff are homosexual in orientation themselves. This can be emotionally distressing for them because they know some of the patients who are being admitted and know what lies ahead for many of them. In Heather's experience the homosexuals on her staff seem more sensitive and empathetic to those patients who are of a like sexual orientation and are able to identify more closely with them. This can add to the stress upon the nurse, however, as the knowledge about their fatal condition is not easy to accommodate.

Because it is a ward where patients stay long term, the staff are able to make better relationships over weeks and months and they get to know their partners and friends too. If they improve and are allowed home, that is considered a great bonus but because of the home care team link, the patients know they can ask to be readmitted speedily.

As a Christian nurse Heather enjoys the fellowship she

can have with some of her staff who are also Christians.
She has experienced some adverse reactions from another
nurse who discovered that Heather is a committed Christian and was all set to take on that AIDS ward. 'Are you
on some kind of crusade?' she asked her suspiciously.
Heather was able to say that was not true. She is a nurse
who happens to be a Christian working in the field of
AIDS. She resists letting insensitive Christians preach at
the patients. Heather knows from her considerable number
of years in the profession that there are gentler, softer
ways of showing Christian concern. Sometimes a patient
may ask her a question about spiritual things and she will
prayerfully take that opportunity for giving spiritual care.
Her policy is never to force anything but to wait for the
right moment – if God wills there will be an opening to
talk about the love of God for them. But as a sister she is
committed to love in action more than words. There are
chaplains who can be asked to visit the ward if necessary.

Her advice to nurses but especially to Christian nurses,
is that they work out how they feel about homosexuality
before they move into AIDS care. 'It is not good to
have to work through those feeling on the ward . . . The
relationships with the patients are intimate, one to one, so
there is need for great sensitivity. In caring for the whole
person, that includes the spiritual as well. The nurses on
my ward do spend more time talking to their patients
than on other wards. They are listening to their patients,
perhaps counselling them, supporting them, trying to cover
every aspect of their needs, especially if that person is
coming to the end of his life.'

In many other ways, the ward functions just as a general
ward with ward rounds by two teams of consultants. There
is also a link with outpatients because for many years the
hospital has run a large clinic for sexually transmitted
diseases. The multidisciplinary team on that ward includes
doctors, social workers, psychologists, home support team
members and the chaplain.

The work of the home support team is invaluable as

many patients come from many different parts of Britain and of the world. The team consists of one senior nurse, a charge nurse, one GP, one welfare rights person, one social worker. They meet with the patient when he is first admitted and then make a point of discovering as much information as they can about his family and home situation. By building up a relationship they then can follow him up when he is sent home. In that way they can make absolutely certain that he has all the help he needs there and is linked up with the local services. The team members are on call all the time, carrying a bleep twenty-four hours a day so that the patients can ring up at any time if in some distress. They can also readmit a patient to the ward in an emergency by ringing the sister. They manage to cover the whole of the London Underground map, which is quite an area to cover!

One unusual aspect of this type of nursing is the need for some psychiatric training. AIDS presents definite psychological symptoms, and as a new ward sister Heather was made aware of her own lack of expertise in this area. She could see that this knowledge would help her to know if a patient was psychologically ill or experiencing psychiatric problems or trauma associated with not being able to cope with the full implications of the diagnosis.

In the community

One new Christian initiative is taking place in the area of AIDS care in the community.

Having previously worked with a terminal care team, Jackie, a District Nurse, was looking for the next step in her career. Then, completely unexpectedly, came the right opportunity – she was asked to join a Christian-based home care agency, AIDS Care Education and Training (ACET). She prayed for confirmation that the post was God's will for her and was convinced that it was. With great anticipation she became a member of the ACET home care team, visiting AIDS patients in their own homes.

She found it a fulfilment of all she had hoped and prayed for. Despite the many sadnesses, there was great joy.

She found herself expected to work from an office based in Ealing near her home. At the start of each week there would be a staff meeting to coordinate other meetings throughout the week for each member of staff – before they spent considerable time in prayer for the week ahead. The fast growing organisation had recently received a fresh injection of funds to help it move forward. Jackie found much satisfaction as a nurse in caring for these patients in their own homes – first assessing their condition, then planning how to control their symptoms and evaluating the care. It was her hope to provide these people with the best in terminal care. Trained volunteers from the local community were also involved in this care and she could always arrange for one of them to visit regularly to do something practical.

Teaching and training were another important part of her work, and she shared with the other staff a heavy programme of speaking engagements around London and the South East. The hardest part of her work was seeing so many young men and women (and babies) who had been diagnosed HIV positive. Many were homosexual, but she kept before her one of Mother Teresa of Calcutta's ideals tested in her amazing work among the destitute and dying to care for each one as if she was caring for Jesus himself.

Another centre for the care of people with AIDS, and Christian-based, is the Mildmay Hospice in the East End of London.

After the old Mildmay Mission Hospital was closed in 1981, there was an enormous furore partly because it had served the local community so well, and partly because it had a large network of committed Christian supporters. In the event, with new supporters and funding it was able to reopen in 1984 with a brief to serve the local community, and relying on various trusts to support the work. Having talked to the local community, the staff sought to meet their request for a unit for young chronic sick and disabled. That opened in 1985, giving hope that the Mildmay still had a role to play. But at that point no one realised what its greater strategic role would be.

They first opened one ward for ten chronic sick and disabled and there were ten beds used as GP beds to send their patients sometimes for respite care or convalescent beds. The number of beds rose to twenty-four by the end of 1985. In 1986 Dr Veronica Moss was appointed to the staff as medical director. She had been partly responsible for setting up at Mildmay a health check service for would-be missionary candidates. That service was run alongside a GP surgery where a Christian doctor had his base.

Unexpectedly, in 1987, CARE Trust approached the staff of the reopened Mildmay with a startling suggestion. Could not the Mildmay be involved in making a Christian response to the growing AIDS threat?

When Ruth Sims, who had been in district nurse management, was interviewed for a post as senior nurse, all this was very new and as yet undeveloped. But she was informed that the entire board of governors had been unanimous in making the decision to say yes to opening an AIDS care hospital. It was in God's amazing provision that Ruth had already done four years' research into quality of life for the dying and terminal care.

There were personal reasons why Ruth believed she would not be offered the post – a broken marriage, and remarriage. But some on the board had recognised that her deeply painful childhood which partly affected her teenage and married years might bring to the Mildmay someone who knew God in the depths, a Christian who had known rejection and the kind of feelings known to many AIDS sufferers. She was offered the job.

Ruth felt that if God could forgive her for what she had done, perhaps she could start forgiving herself. In that happier frame of mind she longed to be able to reach out to AIDS sufferers with the same message. She had known judgment from Christians who had not known the full facts and circumstances – she was hoping to offer acceptance to these patients praying that that loving acceptance would help to change their lives. Too often AIDS patients feel they have been judged and assumptions made about them because of their condition. It was Ruth's desire as she started work at the new Mildmay that they would experience first and foremost love and acceptance which was unconditional.

It was never going to be easy to do this because of the homosexual lifestyle of many AIDS sufferers and some Christians' attitudes towards them. But it was not only from Christians that the Mildmay received criticism but also from homosexual groups who were suspicious of their motives.

There were stark contrasts between the new Mildmay and the old. In the past it had been run as the Mildmay Mission Hospital and every ward sister was expected to stand up and preach the gospel daily at the ward services. At the new Mildmay she believed it was more important to establish a relationship with her patients. Then in a secure, trusting safe relationship, people would share the really fundamental things. She proved this to be true. It had happened and she could speak of many people coming to know the Lord for themselves through this.

'We pray that God will speak to people through the way we care, and that care has to be of the highest professional standard. Next, we must let people understand that we accept them despite what they are and what they may have done. If they are discriminated against, they sense it.' Many of the patients wanted their lovers to visit and find acceptance as well.

Great strides have taken place in the new Mildmay – and none more so than when the Princess of Wales came to visit. On that occasion one of the patients told Princess Diana: 'I have been given the will to live here at the Mildmay. Now, if you can give back to somebody like me the will to live until they die, you are giving them the greatest gift. This is the gift that I have been given here.'

Before they reached the point of finally designing and equipping patients' rooms, a team of staff from the Mildmay flew to San Francisco, USA, to talk to people caring for AIDS patients there and to the patients themselves. Ruth Sims said:

We pride ourselves on the fact that we have always gone to the consumer to check what is best. Thus we did this with AIDS sufferers – we checked with the consumers and said to them 'What do you think?' Our plans were modified accordingly and when we returned, we planned to have nine single rooms with en suite handwash basins and special toilets which flush in a special way. Then, there is no real risk of infection if your nursing practice is good and you have body fluid precautions. I instituted the wearing of gloves and an apron when handling body fluids, whether it is taking away or bringing bed pans, bottles or urinals or doing new dressings. It is clear if you look at the number of people who are being revealed as HIV positive that we just do not know who has got the virus or who has not. The safest thing is to treat everybody as if they have got infected body fluids.

These rules apply on the unit for chronic disabled as well as the one for AIDS, and she believed that there should be a mixing in any case between the two units and the staff too. If they have a concert everyone is invited. The impression the media liked to promote was that people without AIDS do not want to mix with people who do. The opposite is true, and the Mildmay is witness to the fact.

However, nursing AIDS sufferers is a high stress area and it became clear before long that there were many factors which make it different from traditional hospice care. One aspect is the age of the clients – nearly all are young adults in their early twenties. This means they are the same age as the nurses themselves. Also it is a multisystems disease so the symptoms are varied. Caring for AIDS patients may entail coping with torrential diarrhoea, with an ulcerated mouth or ulcerations from the mouth to the anus, with facial lesions and disfigurations or excessive weight loss or psychological distress. Hospices generally are thought to be places where active treatment is no longer a priority. As there is such ignorance medically about treating AIDS, it was expected that many would die. But in fact 53 per cent of Mildmay patients go home actually thanks to the care they received which meant the disease took a different course. There have been remarkable examples of patients being admitted practically moribund, slightly confused, needing two-hourly eye and mouth care, so weak they were unable to turn themselves in bed. Two months later, the same patients would be out of bed, dressed and looking round for a flat so that they could be discharged.

The hospice receives numerous requests for help and many visits of a professional nature. They plan to run short training courses too.

In order to lead the way professionally, the Mildmay staff have done various courses, in particular the one run by Robert Pratt at the Charing Cross Hospital and the RCN course. The nursing care model is entitled 'primary nursing'. This means that a patient has a nurse solely responsible for assessing and planning his care. There are three primary nurses on the units, each with a team of associate nurses and each team looking after one patient. The primary nurse plans the care and the others help to give it. Before a patient is admitted he is invited to come and see the Mildmay. Alternatively, the primary nurse goes to visit him at home or in the other hospital. She or he introduces herself as the nurse at the Mildmay personally responsible for his care. When that patient is admitted, she will welcome him and plan his care. She also plans his discharge. This allows for attention to detail, Ruth maintains. As AIDS is presenting in so many different ways, attention to detail is vital. Above all what these patients need is time. Most of them are articulate and intelligent people who want to direct their own care. Most hospitals tell their patients how they are going to be treated, but at the Mildmay it is the other way round. As general manager of the hospice and director of nursing, Ruth had the opportunity to adopt this approach. But she admits that without enough nurses or equipment and finance, it would be hopeless to attempt doing this.

Her staff-to-patient ratio over a twenty-four-hour period is one nurse to 1.5 patients in the one unit. In the other unit, because the longstay patients will not be so ill, they will have personal care attendants. She is planning to combine the new type of support worker who is to replace the old nursing auxiliary – as per Project 2000 – with an eight-month period of special training beforehand.

Moreover there is the home care team too which she was just setting up in the autumn of 1989, able, she hoped, to care for the patients at home.

It was decided that the nurses in the hospice would wear uniforms though they would be called by their Christian names. The reason for the uniforms was because some of the less well sighted patients (damaged eyesight is one of the ways in which HIV affects them) could not see easily and the uniform was recognised readily by all.

There are various ways in which the hospice's Christian ethos is still evident. The chaplain is one of the management team for a start, which may be a little unusual. He is a Baptist minister. This means that at every weekly management meeting the spiritual side of the work is represented and has its rightful place. Every morning there is an optional meeting of the staff to pray and worship God in the temporary chapel. A permanent chapel is being built. Eventually there will be a time for worship in the afternoon also; currently, afternoon prayers are held on the unit for staff and patients. The head of the home care team is an Anglican deacon and can assist where needed. Every Thursday there is a Communion Service and the Sacraments are then taken up to the units and offered to patients and visitors.

It is exciting to know that spiritual growth takes place in the Mildmay still. One patient who attended an Easter Service was so moved by it that he knew he wanted to give his life to the Lord. It was wonderful that the Mildmay could link him up with the local church and he was subsequently baptised and confirmed. Another joy was to hear about Flo, one of the severely handicapped residents, who had also asked to be baptised. These are just a few illustrations of God's power at work in this place dedicated to Christian care.

Ruth believes that AIDS nursing is the biggest challenge to the profession possibly in its history. It excites her that the Mildmay, a Christian foundation, is seen as a pioneer in this vital area.

12

Running a Ward, and Hospital Management

'In trying to staff the new hospital she was aware that some sisters were so authoritarian she wondered which staff she could possibly ask to work on their wards . . .'
Senior Nurse Manager Elizabeth

To become a sister of a hospital ward today is no sinecure. It demands great organisational skills and the ability to cope with heavy pressure. Some of the sisters I spoke to had found the demands too much and moved elsewhere, or into the community. A few had left nursing altogether. But despite the heavy load of responsibility others receive such job satisfaction that they have no desire to leave. The main areas of unease appear to centre around the fact of being too much office-based rather than ward-based – leading to less patient contact. The other element that raises big questions is – what comes next in their career? Do they move up the promotion ladder – possibly into management?

Jane had been a sister in a big London teaching hospital for some years. She found all the changes in nurse education somewhat bewildering with new names for courses and qualifications. Her task as sister kept changing too, being more office-based than before. Each patient had a buzzer by his bed for calling help so there was much less need to walk up and down her ward. She was shocked by the decision in her hospital that sisters should manage their own ward budgets. She commented, 'If I had wanted to be an accountant I would not have chosen to be a nurse.'

Asked about role models when she became a sister she agreed that she had been impressed by the patience and love evident in some of her senior staff colleagues, particularly when she was training. Looking back to her training in that same hospital, she also recalled some truly tough sisters. 'When I was a student nurse some of them were unbelievable. I spent eight weeks on one ward where the sister was the old-fashioned "stiff and starchy" type who treated her junior staff very frostily. She never smiled, never said thank you, never gave you any praise whatsoever. The only time she opened her mouth was to tell you you had done something wrong. The result was I was petrified of her. The only good thing was that the sluice had two doors and if you came through one door and you saw Sister approaching, you went out by the other door!'

Yet it was on that ward that Jane felt she really learnt how to nurse – and from that sister. She learnt how to make a patient really comfortable. The sister lavished care on the patients. She was a very good nurse even if she was awful to work under. 'Another thing I learnt from her was how *not* to treat my junior nurses.' Unlike that sister, Jane enjoyed working with her staff team and tried to show approval and encouragement especially to any who were finding the going tough. One of her greatest thrills was to see one of her students who had had a fairly difficult time settling down, able eventually to enjoy the job and give something of herself to the patients and the other staff.

With better working practices, better social life and holiday allowances, sisters are not so prone to make their ward the be-all and end-all of their existence, which happened in the past. In contrast, Jane had also worked with a sister who was 'all airy fairy – the complete opposite – and that could be equally frustrating'.

Jane lays great store on a sister being a good team leader and having due consideration for others. They must notice

whether all the staff – from auxiliaries and SENs upwards
– are busy and happy. A relaxed atmosphere might prove
more valuable than a spotless ward on some occasions.
Another important aspect of her work was to spend time
caring not only for patients but for their relatives.

Teaching was also part of her role as a sister. This
entailed seeking to upgrade herself professionally and doing various postgraduate courses. Ward management was
becoming more and more vital but NHS cutbacks had
affected her hospital badly, with many wards being closed
down. The Director of Nursing Service's attitude was, 'we
seem to have got people used to the idea of closure now.'
Jane believed it had the opposite effect of making staff less
committed to their jobs, wondering just when the axe was
going to fall. Some of the immensely useful inter-hospital
services had been cut also – the social worker's post,
fetching blood samples, ward cleaning, taking and collect-
ing the post. In her five years as a sister the amount of
fetching and carrying she had to organise had doubled.
Meanwhile, the intake of patients overall had increased
and the nursing staff were really stretched.

The next step?

After a considerable number of years in a ward situation,
many sisters consider hospital management. Sister Esther
works at a big London hospital as the sister of a general
surgical ward. As a Christian Esther prayed that God
would guide her about her next career move. She has
several strong reasons for believing she was not meant to
move upwards. 'As a sister I enjoy having an influence
over the total care of the twenty-eight patients on my ward
and with my team of staff – six staff nurses and fifteen to
eighteen students. Though I have considered moving on
into management and away from the clinical area, I would
lose that contact with the patients. There is no clinical
management structure as yet, but it will come.'

She feels, however, that it is essential that some Christian nurses do move into senior management – that is one way to have greater influence for good in the hospital.

Besides low staffing levels and NHS cutbacks any sister also faces the threat of strikes. At the time of writing the Royal College of Nursing has refused to sanction strikes. Esther is thankful that most of her ward staff are RCN members. For herself she could not go on strike. She believes it is wrong to withdraw her labour though she has some sympathy with the need for better pay and conditions for nurses. She works incredibly long hours – fifty hours a week – but she does not get paid for the extra. She maintains it is impossible to do the work within the time she is paid for. With the loss of so many nurses from the profession, it is extremely hard to provide continuity of care.

As a sister of a fairly demanding ward, she finds great strength in her church and from close Christian friends to whom she can occasionally unburden herself. It is this spiritual backup that keeps her from losing heart when the pressures prove almost too great.

Many nurses are leaving the profession through pressure of work as much as low pay. Some are disillusioned with nursing altogether. Here sisters can be a listening ear to colleagues who need to pour out some of their frustrations. One sister, Esther spoke of, 'a brilliant sister with tremendous skills of caring and listening and counselling was about to leave nursing for good. She felt she had been put upon and put upon so much she could not take any more. Who could blame her?'

Esther also knew of nurses who had left the profession in disgust but returned to it later because they could not find the same job satisfaction or personal fulfilment anywhere else. She herself still believes it is a wonderful profession to be a part of and she still loves nursing despite all the problems. She continues to battle on with low staffing levels, and as a Christian sister seeks to make good relationships with all the staff – medical, paramedical and nursing.

The example of Elizabeth should encourage those Christian nurses who are reluctant to move up the promotion scale. For her, promotion from her role as a ward sister in a London hospital came when she became a nursing officer. Later she moved to her more recent role as Patient and Nursing Services Manager where two gynaecological hospitals were to be combined into one new hospital. She has found much to rejoice as well as tear her hair out about in the job. A major part of her task is to help her staff in the two older hospitals face up to the full implications of the changes. She has responsibility too for staffing the new hospital – and needs to get to know her staff accordingly. Honesty in management is a great need. Since moving into management she has discovered a great deal of political intrigue. Some staff will even lie to gain precedence over colleagues or an easy way out of a problem. 'If a nurse says she will do something – she must do it. If mistakes have been made, she will not be devious but face up to the consequences and admit them.'

Another important quality in management is the ability to cultivate trust. In her daunting task of helping to bring about the amalgamation of two hospitals into one, Elizabeth recognised that change is unavoidable in all hospitals. But it is not always a bad thing as she proved for herself. She would be no good as a manager if she allowed herself to feel threatened by change or frightened by it. She would be unable to see the potential good of any new ideas. She keeps in mind a BBC *Thought for the Day* she heard to the effect that 'without trust there can be no change'. In her role she has to build up trust with all the staff. Then, if they know that she will not make promises she cannot keep, they should respond in the same way.

Why do some Christian nurses find management hard? 'One of the difficult things for Christian nurse managers is that many nurses do not see themselves rising to the top. They are not naturally ambitious. Yet we especially need Christians in management – in hospital, in local health authorities and in politics etc.'

13

The Pros and Cons of Teaching

'I had always had this dream about being a clinical teacher – right from the start of my training as a nurse . . . I had no idea how many years it would take . . .'
Clinical Teacher Gill

One of the major losses when a nurse moves into the field of education is patient contact, though it is usually possible to integrate ward experience and practical teaching with the lecture room, so that it is not lost altogether.

One of the marked ambivalences among nurses concerns the current upgrading of the profession with the new academic thrust in their education and greater emphasis placed on lecture-room theory as opposed to hands-on care. The fact that more and more university and polytechnic courses will replace hospital-based courses in the near future only adds to this unease as Project 2000 makes its impact.

Furthermore, there is going to be the phasing out of the state enrolled nurse completely – another symbol of the current attempt to improve the profession academically. But at what cost?

And herein lies the dilemma. Many state enrolled nurses chose that particular qualification because it kept them by the bedside where they wanted to be. But, as SEN Kim, who qualified recently in Leicester knows, already the very training that she undertook has ceased. It is some comfort to know that the desperate shortages of staff means she can remain as an SEN with a job to do for a number of years. However, if she decides to make something of her career as a nurse, she must retrain and convert her qualification to the equivalent of an RGN, which is easier said than done. First, she has to gain the same entrance qualifications by going to evening classes. Second, she has to apply to do a year long conversion course, of which there are far too few. For example, in Leicester where Kim made enquiries about the course it was desperately oversubscribed with fifteen places offered and 400 applicants.

Hilary, who has been teaching one such SEN conversion course in Manchester, explained the dilemma further. In Manchester only those SENs who had had a year's experience on the ward could apply to convert. Even so, for a year's intake of ten places there were 150 applications.

The course ran in fact for fifty-nine weeks and was based in south Manchester but moved round the city to give the nurses varied clinical experience, including working in the community. If they passed the examination, they gained an RGN certificate and could then apply for staff nurse posts for which SENs were not usually qualified.

Hilary agreed that the real problem was Project 2000 which tells the SENs they are no longer academically acceptable and will consequently be restricted in the jobs they can apply for and their promotion prospects will look bleak. Yet, while Project 2000 is being implemented 'we are going to be needing those enrolled nurses desperately to fill the staff gaps, especially as there is a shortage of RGNs coming into the profession because of the demographic drop in recruits.'

Before she taught the conversion course for SENs Hilary was a nurse tutor working with student nurses. There was quite a contrast – the SENs on the conversion course were all extremely well motivated to complete the course. Indeed some were so anxious to do well it actually affected their performance. She had some sympathy with them. Many of them had chosen to be SENs because they saw it as a way to give bedside care which they preferred. 'For some of them I think it is the more appropriate role because they have not got the academic ability to convert to RGN. Maybe it is not appropriate that they should. Other SENs have been given misinformation at the start of their careers and did not realise fully that doing a two year SEN course might restrict them in the long term.'

The problem, as summarised by her, is that at a rough estimate, in 1989 there were seventy or eighty schools of nursing which ran a conversion course. 'Thus a few hundred SENs are qualifying as RGNs. But we need many many more conversion courses to meet the need. And I suspect that finance comes into this as well – because the newly upgraded SENs to RGNs will have to be paid better. I personally believe most of them are very able nurses and deserve the better pay and job prospects.'

There were some doubts in Hilary's mind however as to whether the course would continue in its present shape if at all. One startling suggestion had been made that all SENs should automatically be converted to RGN and it is indisputable that many SENs have been doing the work of RGNs on the wards due to the chronic staff shortages.

There is no ambivalence in Hilary's feelings about the current emphasis on academic input in nursing. 'No, I don't think nursing has become too academic. The profession itself has become much more technical and computerised. There is greater need for a knowledge of research methods and how to find and use statistics for instance. This academic input should never be at the expense of good practical nursing care.'

Becoming a tutor

Hilary herself made the transition to teaching a little reluctantly for a number of reasons. 'I really loved nursing and did not want to teach for that reason.' In a sense the reasons for her becoming a tutor were negative ones, yet they reveal the heart of the problems and pressures facing many sisters in Britain's hospitals – the stress created by too much work to do on a busy ward and too little time to do it and not enough staff or resources to cover the ward properly.

Becoming a nurse tutor means considerable loss of patient contact and Hilary missed that. Yet she found her contact with her students replaced it. Ultimately, she said, 'The patients are still your concern and the reason for your being there as a tutor. In the overall pattern that is why you are teaching – hopefully to improve patient care.'

Instead of the successful running of a ward, examination results become a prime motivator. 'Also you care a good deal about your students' welfare – as you slowly get to know them as people you are more concerned for them as individuals and not mere examination fodder.'

Nurse education has undergone huge changes while she has been teaching over the past few years. Each hospital now designs its own three year RGN courses which vary in content and curriculum accordingly. There is the new and increased emphasis on community care as well as health education, communication and various sociological philosophies. The Nursing Process has also become part and parcel of what she teaches too. She feels that from a teaching point of view it is a very good way to teach, from a problem solving model, treating the patient more as a person. 'We look at the patient as a whole, with more emphasis on psychology and sociology and some recognition that they have spiritual needs too.'

But she sensed on the negative side that there was a more humanistic approach to teaching nursing which excluded that spiritual element. 'Quite a few of the modern secular philosophies focus more on the human being as the be-all and end-all. As if the individual is the one that the world revolves around to the exclusion of God. I believe we need more mature Christians in senior hospital management and in the planning of nurse education in the future.

I think Christians in nursing need to get their act together professionally. We have got to be prepared to make a stand on some of these humanistic issues. Yet we have got to do it in such a way that it is acceptable and not narrow and dogmatic.'

Another kind of teacher in our hospitals has a different role in nurse education. Clinical teaching is not classroom-based but centred in the ward situation. A nurse tutor like Hilary is usually working in the School of Nursing – while a clinical teacher operates on the wards, though in liaison with the school. Clinical teachers usually have to have more than one higher qualification in order to fulfil the role.

Gill had always hoped to become a clinical teacher one day. But she had to work exceptionally hard to achieve that goal for a number of reasons, some of them personal. She had become a Christian while working on a neonatal unit in Birmingham after qualifying as a registered sick children's nurse at Great Ormond Street Hospital in London.

But what kept me going was the fact that I had always dreamt about becoming a clinical teacher one day, right from the start of my training as a nurse. You have to be quite advanced up the professional ladder first and you need to have spent at least two years as a sister before you can qualify.

This is not an easy area to get into because clinical teaching is quite different from other kinds of teaching. Clinical teachers work on the wards with the students and with the patients. Usually you have a group of six students to teach, but often you work one to one which is great. I enjoy doing it because you do not lose the patient contact and are still using the nursing skills you have learned. This is a fast developing field in fact. In some units they sometimes swop roles – six months as a sister and six months as a clinical teacher.

Because Gill is married and has an adopted child, she has had to earn her qualifications for this job the long way round and by part-time study. It should have required a six month full-time course, but, because of her personal circumstances, it took her two years to do the Diploma in Nursing, then a further two years to do the Teacher's Certificate at a local Polytechnic either in Birmingham or Leicester. For her it seemed right, if longwinded. But she has had to help earn some money, also, by doing some part-time bank nursing on night duty three nights a week, working on a neonatal special unit on the paediatric bank of nurses.

Then, she added, she had to face the fact that in five years time she was not even sure clinical teachers would still be in post! There would probably be only one grade of teacher in the rapidly changing pattern of nurse education. Nonetheless she hopes to do a degree – a BSc in Health Studies – on a day release basis in Northampton. Once that is completed and her child is older and less dependent, she looks forward to becoming a part-time teacher of nursing.

Midwife teachers

Another type of teaching which takes place in hospital is the work of the midwife teacher. Having reiterated the fact that midwifery has a separate and distinct identity from nursing, it is still relevant here to stress the vital importance of training plenty of midwives for society in general. This is especially true since the numbers who leave the profession after qualifying is very high.

Most midwives find midwifery thrilling and rejoice to see a healthy baby delivered and the joy of the parents afterwards. Becoming a midwife teacher enables the midwife still to operate on the wards when she teaches and of course in the various out-patient clinics. In the antenatal and postnatal clinics she oversees the work of her midwife pupils as they work with the women they are responsible for.

Christine had been doing midwifery overseas before she made the decision to become a tutor. She was aware that becoming a midwife teacher meant a complete change of job. Although she was still working in the same hospital, it did not mean she would be doing the same job. Teaching was quite different. Instead of being attached to one ward, as a tutor she was expected to work between wards and meet the mums-to-be in the clinics beforehand as well as on the wards. 'I discovered I could still go on the neonatal unit but I could not go on the labour wards. In fact, it was more likely that I would be teaching on the antenatal and postnatal wards because on the labour ward there had to be a one-to-one relationship between woman and midwife which excluded the tutor and students.' Some midwife teachers, though, will work a shift in labour wards every so often in order to become the midwife for an individual woman and a role model for a student midwife.

Looking back on those months of learning to teach, she admitted that a certain degree of toughness helped her to weather the classroom and lecture room demands.

In fact, her next post was at Queen Charlotte's in West London – one of the top maternity hospitals in the country. Christine had always wanted to work in London and when she saw a vacancy at Charlotte's she applied. She had become a Christian as a teenager through her local church in the Wirral. Now she prayed that God would confirm that this new and rather scary appointment was right. Imagine her joy, when the senior midwife teacher and she discovered they both knew Christian friends at a mission hospital in Zambia and had many other things in common.

In fact Margaret was a lovely Christian and she helped to make me feel a little more at home in that rather auspicious place. Then a few weeks later I had the formal interview and I got the job. I was thrilled – really excited, though I felt I might have to work extremely hard to maintain high professional standards.

What was good was that all the other tutors had more experience than me. There were probably over a hundred midwives on the staff and we had ten students in each intake. Every three months a new intake started. The course lasted a year though it has been changed to eighteen months since. We tutors also had a say in the selection of the pupil midwives.

The reason why I say it was good that the others had had more experience than me is because I was the only new tutor and I could be supported by the others. Although I felt I was selling my pupil midwives somewhat short because I was so new, I did have help. Some of the subjects I was teaching were totally new to me and had not been covered on the courses I had done. Embryology, for instance, and fetal circulation was another I had hardly touched. The physiology of jaundice also I had never done before; the rhesus factor was another.

As she suspected she did have to work very hard at Charlotte's. On the other hand it was just as well. From her observations of other new tutors, she realised how hard it is for the first couple of years for everyone.

After leaving Queen Charlotte's, Christine went to Uganda to work for the Church Missionary Society as a midwife tutor. But, sadly, this was not a total success and she returned to the United Kingdom after eighteen months. She managed to find a post as a midwife teacher in Leicester glad to note that her new hospital and home town catered for people of all races and cultures. She even met Ugandan women who knew the hospital where she had been working. After a very hard couple of years or so, things began to look up as she made her home in Leicester and found new friends.

Professionally too, she was encouraged to upgrade herself in the large hospital of 1000 beds, 180 of which were maternity. They managed to handle 6000 deliveries a year, so there was no lack of need for new midwives. She had been made responsible for a new intake of fourteen midwife students every four months, but that changed eventually to twelve students every three months.

With her new home settled and a good church, she could turn her mind to doing some part-time study on various day release courses in order to gain a Bachelor of Education degree from Huddersfield Polytechnic using a grant obtained from the Royal College of Midwives. Health education is really the field she is interested in when she has completed a Master's degree at Warwick University.

Nonetheless over her years of academic progress, she has not forgotten her own panics as a brand new tutor. Christine remembers coming across one of the new tutors at Leicester tearing her hair out just a few moments before going home time. Next day she had to teach embryology for the very first time. 'I said, "I'm teaching embryology tomorrow with the neonatal students, why don't we combine the two groups and I'll teach it?" She was thrilled – as a fellow Christian I was the answer to her prayer. At some stage she would have to teach that subject but there seemed no reason why, with only minimal preparation, she should have to be landed with it when I could do it for her. But I could recall my own experience at Charlotte's, otherwise I might not have acted in that way.'

New developments

In any hospital that trains nurses a good deal of the teaching falls on the shoulders of the sister. Ideally the sister or charge nurse should upgrade themselves in some way, and this is where the new emphasis on refresher courses is becoming more and more common. All staff are now encouraged to do refresher courses – if they can find the time and energy. A much broader concept of nurse education is the coming thing. It is planned to provide integrated courses at colleges of health studies where nurses, physiotherapists, radiographers and social workers – all the paramedicals too – can be trained together.

Sisters who want to teach are asked to qualify too. It is normal for them to do City and Guilds certificate 730 or a National Board course in teaching and assessing in clinical practice, in England numbered 997.

One such is Sister Heather who works in a big London teaching hospital. These courses gave her both communication skills and improved the preparation and demonstration of her lectures. It is the norm now for sisters to be teaching on the wards more and more.

In Australia the same obtains. One Australian tutor, Barbara, discovered that though she enjoyed nursing the patients, teaching ultimately gave her greater satisfaction and was God's plan for her. Through it she was led into new professional areas of expertise.

Having trained in Melbourne as an RGN, she did midwifery in Sydney and became a staff midwife on a labour ward. She adored that but it gave her her first taste for teaching. To do a tutor's course she had to go to night school and take two matriculation subjects – physics and economics. This was while she was working as a midwife and on nights, so she became extremely tired. So exhausted was she that she fell asleep bending over a pregnant woman when listening to the fetal heartbeat. She came to suddenly to find someone shaking her and asking if she was all right! However, the extra study was well worthwhile as it qualified her to take the tutor's course later.

First, she did a spell as a district nurse in Sydney and then became a clinical teacher in one of Sydney's biggest teaching hospitals. Still unsure she had the teaching gift, she wanted confirmation from God and her colleagues. When she eventually took the one year tutor's course at the College of Nursing and her subsequent teaching practice went well, Barbara was convinced she was meant to be a tutor. In 1970 she started her teaching career but by that time other concerns were to take her out of hospital teaching into a wider sphere. Like many other nurses of her generation who have to take academic and upgrading courses at a later stage in their careers, Barbara discovered she preferred to be stretched in that way – to learn, to think and question for herself. She saw that as a reflection not only on herself but also on the kind of RGN training she had done in Melbourne in 1962–5. 'Everything was learnt by rote – we learnt anatomy just like you learn Latin verbs.'

On the tutor's course, she met some excellent new teaching role models. One was a physiology tutor who made physiology 'alive and related it to us. That was an exciting discovery.'

Barbara went on to teach for a couple of years in Sydney, but she also became more and more involved with the Australian equivalent of the Nurses' Christian Fellowship – and was then a member of the Council for New South Wales. The NCF had seen and heard her teaching sessions on her special subject, Spiritual Care, and wanted her to move around Australia sharing that particular aspect with other Christian nurses. Thus, in 1972 Barbara moved out of full-time hospital teaching to part-time in order to become a part-time professional developments officer for NCF. By 1974 she was being invited to run a fast growing number of workshops on spiritual care and to travel as a visiting lecturer. It excited her that the nursing profession worldwide was taking notice of what she was teaching and she began to travel in order to share her special concerns on this subject. In due course she found herself based in Britain. Her God-given teaching skills had proved their value again and again. She is a shining example of the exciting opportunities that present themselves to nurses who decide to move into teaching.

14

Nursing in the Community

'As a Christian I find it a privilege to be able to visit people at home and get involved with their families . . .'
District Nurse Marilyn

Project 2000 heralds a new emphasis on community nursing. 'We are trying to view the total patient care in the context of care in the community – not just short spells in hospital. The main thrust will be preventive . . .' Dame Audrey Emerton, Chairwoman of the United Kingdom Central Council.

There are many advantages as a nurse in working in the community. Seeing the patient in his or her own surroundings can help to ascertain their special needs or areas of risk. Linked to a GP surgery, a health clinic or centre, district nurses, health visitors, community midwives, or community psychiatric nurses, work to improve the quality of life of patients and, if possible, help to keep them out of hospital.

Being a district nurse in a rural area provides its fair share of unexpected crises and challenges. This is what District Nurse Ann found in Surrey and Sussex. After experience as an RGN Anne decided God was guiding her into nursing in the community and she did one of the new college courses.

It was a splendid course and I found it refreshing to be a student again – not quite the oldest in a group of twenty-five. There was a great deal of sharing; we all had a contribution to make and helped one another. The two weeks I spent in the community with my practical work teacher, prior to commencing training, were of tremendous benefit. Although I was termed a 'direct entry student' those few days enabled me to make sense of what would otherwise have lacked meaning.

The district nurse is responsible for deciding on the nursing care each patient requires and for seeing that this is carried out. She is part of the Primary Health Care Team which is an interdependent group of medical practitioners, secretaries and receptionists, health visitors, district nurses, and midwives . . . pooling knowledge to provide an effective service. The district nurse teaches patients and relatives to cope for themselves. She frequently works alone and most decisions made are based on her own professional judgment.

Unlike my hospital colleagues I am able to see patients in their own environment where, hopefully, they can retain their own identity. I am therefore a guest in their home. My uniform could be described as protective – perhaps it also gives me power. Alone in the home I am in a vulnerable position. I therefore continually try to see the possible outcome of my actions and to what extent they may be open to misinterpretation.

Teaching opportunities are numerous and must be used if patients are to be nursed around the clock and assisted back to full or partial function . . . I make my initial assessment and attempt to ascertain the amount of knowledge and skill patients have and their attitudes to the situation. Patients with diabetes who require insulin can very often be taught to cope with no outside help and it is rewarding to watch their confidence grow. One hundred-unit insulin has obviously simplified the actual 'drawing-up' – no longer is it necessary to determine strength in relation to dosage. Some patients can learn to anticipate imbalances and take action accordingly, thus maintaining a very reasonable quality of life and independence.

For the carers in the home the district nurse must be on the alert for signs of their overfatigue and mounting anxiety. Unfortumately, there is often little that can be done apart from making time for these feelings to be expressed. The majority of my patients are in the 75 plus age group and their problems are often multiple, further increased when the carer is in a similar age group.

The Nursing Process provides a helpful structure from which to develop an effective care plan. But, when attempting to initiate change, I need to examine my own feelings to ascertain to what extent they are influencing my course of action. Sometimes I fail to strike the right balance between my own personal needs and the patient's wishes. I have to let the patient 'live dangerously!' . . .

It is possible over a period of time to become almost a part of the family. So much so that it is sometimes difficult to discharge a patient when physical help is no longer needed, but it is obvious that moral support and encouragement would be appreciated. Support visits can be planned but may become out of hand in terms of sheer numbers. I have to monitor my case load very carefully.

It is a joy and easy to share my Christian faith with those patients who have some manifestation of theirs in their home, and this is often a source of great delight. However, I well remember, when a ninety year-old gentleman and I had shared our love of the Lord. He then insisted on having a 'word of prayer'. At each pause I said 'Amen' and made to move – but he had put himself between me and the door and continued to pray for about forty minutes.

I believe the most rewarding aspect of my job is caring for the patient who is dying – and his or her family. There are many patients who choose to die at home and

I feel exceedingly privileged to be involved in such care.
It seems to me that a patient will initially have a fear of
dying which gradually subsides as the weeks pass. Some
patients, too, with support, are even able to talk very
positively about their approaching death and those closest to them are able to let them do so. Often a depth of
understanding develops between partners which was not
previously experienced. When a death is expected it is
frequently possible to support the carers in the anticipat-
ory phase of their grief. They can be assisted to talk
through their fears and what life will be like without the
person for whom they have been caring . . .

More recently I have moved my post, and if district
nursing on the edge of Surrey was semirural, then this
part of Sussex where I have been is very rural. I work
much more on my own and miss the support and friendship of my ex-colleagues. My new car takes the unmade
rural roads in its stride but it gets extremely dirty and
needs a weekly clean which it doesn't get. It would seem
I may clock up about 1,000 miles a month in the course
of my duties. I am inclined to feel aggressive behind the
wheel, and I feel my stress level rising when I am unable
to pass a slowly moving farm vehicle! As in my last post,
I am attached to a GP practice. Patients are referred to
me by the doctors and those who are leaving hospital by
the ward sister . . .

Last year I undertook a Practical Work Teacher's
Course at the University of Surrey and found it most
stimulating. Since then I have had district nurse students
allocated to me and thoroughly enjoyed the experience.
We shared a great deal though I felt certain I learned
most.

District Nurse Marilyn has worked in and around Manchester and Salford. Latterly because she is married with a
small child, she prefers to work part-time. She is a treatment room sister in the mornings and a relief district nurse
in the afternoons. Having already trained as a nurse, she

applied to do a shortened training – four months, including a week of study and time spent accompanying a district nurse. When she first qualified, she was single, and began her full-time district nursing career in a very rough area of Manchester where there were blocks of grim, fortress-like maisonettes, desolate and neglected. They became the haunt of drug addicts and drunks. Her task was to visit and care for people who were too ill to cope on their own. Many of them had cancer, or bad ulceration of the legs. 'I visited them at home to give them injections or to do dressings for them. The GP I was attached to referred them to me, often after they had been discharged from hospital. Some needed stitches removing and then fresh dressings done. Or if a patient became too ill to be nursed at home, we sought to find them a hospital place, but it was not always easy.'

Marilyn cared for patients who had been disabled by strokes and needed looking after at home. The carer, a relative, also needed advice and support to adapt to the disability of a husband or wife. As a Christian nurse she found it a privilege to be able to visit people at home with their family close at hand. 'Naturally you got involved with their families much more easily than in hospital. I enjoy that relationship you can make with patients on the district . . . They get to know you well when you are visiting daily and feel they can trust you . . . The district nurse's uniform is important – and usually people respect it. I certainly loved the opportunity to work one-to-one with a patient at home and not feel I had to relate to a whole ward.'

Alertness is a very necessary quality in a district nurse. Marilyn tended one woman who had been discharged from hospital after a major gynae operation. The first time she visited her and tended the wound the woman looked ghastly. She continued to look so awful that Marilyn decided to check her blood pressure – an unusual procedure as district nurses do not always have the equipment. The woman admitted that she had a stomach pain and had fainted recently. As soon as Marilyn took her blood pressure and saw how low it was she rang her doctor. He came, and immediately rang for an ambulance. The woman was bleeding internally and would have died had she not been speedily returned to hospital.

Marilyn said, 'I believe God had his hand upon me in a special way that day – it was a miracle that I visited her in time. I thank God I acted as I did and quickly and had the right piece of equipment to take that woman's blood pressure.'

The role of the district nurse will be changing soon with the arrival of practice nurses in GP surgeries. The introduction of practice nurses can make the health visitors and district nurses feel threatened. 'When I am at the GP clinic on my own' says Marilyn, 'I see about twelve patients. When the Practice Nurse is there I see only four.'

The emphasis in care for the elderly too is moving from the ward to care in the community – and some wards have been closed. 'We feel,' Marilyn adds, 'we will be left as district nurses to care for the people the hospitals do not want to take – the elderly and the bedfast.' That was not what she, for one, had hoped to be doing as a district nurse.

The work in the community is to change even more radically in the future. With Project 2000 to be implemented, the community is to take on more and more of the health care burden.

As in hospital there is a management structure in the community, and Christians are able to bring spiritual maturity to this area of the profession, as they do to other areas. Margaret was a late entrant to district nursing. She had left nursing to marry and bring up a family. Recently she was appointed a senior nurse for district nurses, managing some forty district nurses in quite a large area of Middlesex. This means she is office-based and no longer doing clinical nursing, but able to give an overview of the current situation and the introduction of practice nurses.

I believe that district nurses have got to be careful about

what they do and don't do because they will end up doing themselves out of a job. GPs will be able to employ their own district nurses in future. The full implication of that is still being worked out. At present the GP finds it quite lucrative to have a practice nurse. The practice gets some 70 per cent of her salary back from the Family Practice Committee. If she does enough immunisations or cervical smears she has earned her keep.

Ideally the district nurse and the practice nurse should work in harness together and support each other . . . If a patient comes into a GP's surgery or health centre and needs attention on the spot, the practice nurse should see him. The district nurse's role is to go out and visit the patients at home, especially those who cannot come to surgery for care. It is also the GP's responsibility to encourage the district nurses to develop professionally.

Margaret found the move from the community into management was not easy. 'You no longer visit the clients as you once did, and you miss them. Over the years you become used to forming relationships with your clients and receiving approval from them. This makes you feel happy and glad to have been of help. In management you do not get the same input from the patients and I found that the worst part of my change of job and the most difficult transition to make. Though in my experience, patients were more appreciative in hospital than at home.'

She emphasises that district nurses have to remember that in the home they are visitors. In hospital the reverse is true. It is the patients who are in strange surroundings and the nurses in their own domain.

With the moves away from expensive acute care – particularly for the elderly in hospital – towards better care for patients at home, community-based carers have taken on a new significance. The Nursing Process helped district nurses to view their patients as a whole. For Margaret, who had done her RGN in the 1960s, she experienced the Nursing Process for the first time when training as a district nurse. 'I found it such a revelation! It made a nurse's life much easier. Suddenly you knew what you were doing – the assessment and documentation was much better. You were giving the patient what was the best care for each individual.'

Health visiting had formerly been involved chiefly in caring for children from babies to five-year-olds. Today it is more concerned with prevention on a much wider scale, caring for people of all ages. Margaret hopes that the two disciplines will continue to work in cooperation with each other and other community-based carers.

The new name for district nurses will be national district nurses (NDNs). In the future there will be a need for more workers in the community. There are already several groups of qualified nurses financed from sources other than the NHS. MacMillan Nurses are one highly regarded group, financed by the charity, the MacMillan Trust. There is a growing movement towards nursing AIDS sufferers at home and many Christians work in these home care teams.

Occupational health is a growing force which should not be forgotten in the battle for better health. Nurses are being employed by companies – in industry, to provide a service for their workforce. Usually they are based in an occupational health centre within the factory or office complex. Most seem to provide care for minor ailments and accidents and would always call upon a doctor's advice for anything more major.

Health visitors

Health visitors still provide a mainstay in the community setting. Working in harness with district nurses and community midwives they are usually based in health centres. Health Visitor Enid from Liverpool had first-hand experience of some hair-raising events during the Toxteth riots:

As Christian nurses we ought to have the security of knowing that we are in the place where God wants us to be. For some community nurses it may be in a beautiful rural area or a pleasant old market town. But for me it is in the inner city of Liverpool.

The area in which I work has sadly made headlines several times in the national newspapers and on television because of rioting. In 1981 and 1982 buildings were burned, vehicles overturned, roads barricaded, shops looted, police injured with missiles and masonry. It appeared, via the media, that Toxteth was a stronghold of violent anarchy. For those of us who live in a reasonably normal environment nearby, it is difficult to imagine the devastation that surrounded me that Monday morning in July 1981. I found it difficult to comprehend what I saw as I was diverted by numerous policemen before I arrived at my health clinic. I was saddened by the result of lawlessness against authority, what I believed to be man's greed for material possessions and the obvious forces of evil that had been at work the previous night. As I wept over the destruction I gained a deeper understanding of how Jesus must have felt when we read that He wept over Jerusalem (Luke 19:41). That City was a sacred place to the Jewish people; it was loved and respected, but Jesus knew that disaster would eventually come – thus He looked on the City with a heavy and saddened heart.

These were the feelings of many people in our city during those days of unrest. Which building would be the next target of aggression? During this time, the community nursing services continued to function . . . There were many patients, both sick and elderly, needing care and attention. There were families with young children who lived over shops which had been burnt to the ground. Health visitors tried to locate them, particularly those with very young babies. Some had left home so quickly that neighbours were not even sure where they had gone.

We had to move our night nursing service, from the Toxteth area, to enable them to continue their work

with as little disturbance as possible. Prior to the disturb-
ances in the city it had become necessary for district
nurses on their late calls to be 'escorted'. We have all
seen our society's moral and ethical standards change,
and people are no longer concerned about loving their
neighbour. We found there was no longer any respect
for the district nurse even in uniform. No thought was
given by some young people to cars which belonged to
community nurses. Many were broken into and stolen
during the course of their duties. Recently one car was
actually stolen from a family health clinic car park.

Enid admits that health visiting in the inner cities may not
seem attractive to some people. In this area health visiting
may involve dealing with people who are inadequate,
unable to cope with the pressures, demands and strains of
family life. The health visitor may become frustrated when
confronted with apparent apathy, and may despair if the
support given to a specific problem family brings no im-
provement. But the health visitor may be the first to notice,
for example, deterioration of care given to children in
certain families, and she will experience a kind of satisfaction in being involved and helping at the outset with such
cases.

When assessing a student health visitor during her supervised practice in an inner city, Enid says:

I pay particular attention to one of the questions: 'Has
she the ability to show an attitude of acceptance to
clients of all types?' This I consider to be an important
aspect of health visiting. It is a principle which ought to
be adhered to not only by health visitors but also by
Christians wherever they are working. It should be a
challenge to us as Christian nurses when we see the
principles which were taught by the Lord Jesus Christ
being carried out with consideration and compassion by
people who may not adhere to our Christian belief and
doctrine. I learned from my experience of the Toxteth

riots that our place of work ought to be important to us
– for prayer as well as action. Whatever may be done to
improve the inner cities, the problems will remain, unless
the hearts and lives of the people are changed through
the indwelling love and power of our Lord Jesus Christ.

Abortion aftercare makes up a considerable proportion of
any health visitor's case load. Robert was a health visitor
outside Manchester. He discovered that abortion pre-care
and aftercare soon occupied a good deal of his time. He
found that along with the team of health care workers,
they were expected to counsel and advise women seeking
to have abortions. It was not a simple task – none of
the options the women faced were easy. Too often, he
believed, abortion was presented as the 'easy' solution to
unwanted pregnancy, when very often it was not. On the
other hand, he realised it might not be 'easy' to have the
baby. He recalls some examples – one of a twenty-one-
year-old single girl living at home whose pregnancy had
resulted from a short-lived relationship with a man. Her
mother was adamant that the girl should have an abortion,
but the daughter wanted to have the baby. Robert's difficult role was to mediate between them. 'I tried to support
the girl while at the same time seeking not to alienate her
mother, because it would be extremely hard for that girl
to cope if she had the baby and her mother kicked her out.
In the end, the mother came round and she became a
grandmother.'

Many health visitors teach – in schools, youth clubs or
women's groups – wherever there is the opportunity to
promote preventive medicine. It could be on drugs and
avoiding drug abuse – it could be on contraception or it
might be teaching young mums about parenting. If the
battle for good health is to be won in the community,
teaching preventive medicine is essential. To train health
visitor students, the health visitor can attend a field work
teachers' course. Edith fairly late in her nursing career
took that option. Having qualified as an RGN in Durham

and become a sister, she left Britain to work as a nurse in Canada and found she matured and gained an immense amount in her time overseas. She admitted that as a community midwife in Wiltshire she had not been impressed by working in the community. That did not deter her from applying to become a health visitor. She chose to train in Southampton and was thrilled to get to know a very strong group of Christians as fellow students at the university and in the local churches. She also became involved with The Navigators and during her time in the city she learnt a great deal about personal evangelism. And she enjoyed her health visiting. 'I felt it used the whole of my personality and experience, not just my bedside nursing. I loved visiting the clients in their own homes. You related to the patients at a different level. In my SRN training back in the sixties, we were not encouraged to go out into the community, except for the odd day out with a health visitor. It was great to be able to choose to do the options I wanted to do and I thoroughly enjoyed the course.'

She discovered then her preference for preventive medicine. There was a marked contrast between the attractive area where the students lived and that of many of their clients. She was based in one of the grottiest estates in Portsmouth for her practical work experience. Many different nationalities and cultures rubbed shoulders with seamen's families in wretched housing. Later she worked as a student in Southampton and again helped to care for a very mixed group of clients in a child health clinic.

Having qualified, she remained for five years in Southampton before moving to Bristol. It was normal for the health visitors to wear blue and carry an identity card to use if there were problems in gaining entry into a home. As with other health visitors she worked from a health centre which was newly opened and had all the latest modern facilities. It was much larger than any she had been associated with previously. The health visitors occupied one wing with the birth register. Above them were the social workers and there were also occupational and speech therapists, psychiatric nurses and probation officers among the staff. This resulted in superb liaison between the various disciplines represented. In the large reception area there was an age/sex register for all the clients – quite a rare thing in those days. This meant they could ascertain the vulnerable members of their clientèle. Today this register would be computerised. All the rooms were connected by an intercom so that they could communicate within the complex.

After working in Bristol for several years, Edith decided she had done everything in the case load: 'I felt I needed more stimulation professionally and decided to move into education.' Against some stiff competition she was awarded a secondment to do a health visitors teachers' course in Bolton, Lancashire. There were five health visitors among those taking the course and she greatly appreciated the Christians she knew among them. Afterwards she became a field work teacher in Manchester, then began to teach health visitors at the polytechnic. She found the going quite tough. She had to improve her academic qualifications and began studying for a Master of Arts degree. In Edith's view, there would always be a problem for any nurse wishing to teach at a higher level – without a degree they would be discouraged from applying. But doing a degree while holding down a teaching job took a huge amount of commitment in time and energy. She discovered she enjoyed the teaching, though she missed the one-to-one relationships she had built up with her patients as a health visitor. And she still did one day a week in the field with her students so was not completely lecture-room bound.

Private care for the elderly

One Christian nurse, Pat, was a pioneer in the field of private care for the elderly. She was appointed in a kind of job share scheme to organise taking elderly patients from NHS hospitals in her district and placing them in private nursing homes. Her title was Placement Liaison Sister and though she was attached to one large hospital she served several. If the patient had a carer looking after him or her the placement liaison sister merely gave advice. If there was no carer at home, she took the place of that relative or friend and after assessing the requirements of each elderly patient and visiting each nursing home, advised which one was most suitable. Eventually she would arrange a visit to the nursing home and help sort out the finances. New government funds had been made available to provide more private nursing homes to care for the elderly, at first for those aged sixty-five and upwards but later extended to include people aged fifty-five.

All this was to enable the NHS to close hospital beds for the long-term elderly patients. There was a great deal about the scheme that troubled Pat. It demanded great tact and sensitivity and good relationships with clients, GPs, social workers, district nurses, health visitors and ward staff in the hospitals. She knew too that if it was successful many other health authorities would copy the idea. It concerned her that these private nursing homes were too often run to make money and not to give proper care. Some people opened a string of nursing homes and she felt the caring aspect too easily became lost.

A great deal of pressure had been put on Pat by the hospital ward staff and by consultants who wanted to empty the longstay beds as soon as possible. They made her feel that she did not have enough time to give the patients proper assessment as to whether or not they could actually manage at home. 'I felt we were just filling up private nursing home beds without giving the patients a chance to make it on their own.' In the private nursing homes there were often not enough trained nursing staff. Many were agency nurses moonlighting from their work at a local hospital and she felt that the patients received little real continuity of care. Pat had experience of caring for elderly patients and her deep uncertainty about what was being done finally caused her to resign from the post.

15

Nursing Overseas

'The missionary nurse in the 1990s operates in a changing world. In many developing countries there is no longer a shortage of trained nurses . . .'
Laurence Dopson, Nursing Times

A huge proportion of nurses who serve overseas are Christians. In the Nurses' Christian Fellowship membership over 200 are missionaries – and over thirty have worked overseas for more than twenty-five years. Not all are hospital nurses. Some are running health education programmes and immunisation schemes or feeding programmes in refugee clinics. Some are teachers who may be training a wide variety of nurses, midwives or paramedicals. Overseas, the Christian nurse or midwife may find herself at the start of something totally new, helping to pioneer new kinds of community care or treatment. This demands planning, good preparation and plenty of patience and prayer.

Barbara serves with the Methodist Church Overseas.

Since I arrived at my present post in Kenya I have experienced extremes of emotions. But underlying all was a deep peace and joy, knowing that I was doing what God wanted for me. We run an extremely busy 130 bed hospital with an equally busy OPD, with no daytime electricity and no treated water . . . I had heard the extended role of the nurse being discussed in the UK before I came to Africa. About ten weeks after I had arrived there was an emergency admission: three men who had received bullet wounds. It was 11 p.m. and the doctors were busy in theatre putting in a chest drain and I was asked to catheterise the man who had received gunshot wounds in the pelvic region. The stock reply 'But I've never done it before!' came to my lips, but not out of my mouth. I attempted it. After all I had assisted doctors many times to do the procedure. Imagine my horror when the man howled with pain, especially as I knew by then that African men are renowned for their stoicism in the face of pain. I was very relieved later to find that the doctor also had difficulties. Fortunately the man recovered some time later, having received trauma to the urinary tract from the bullet wound and not the catheter.

As a tutor in an African hospital I get far more clinical experience than I did in the UK. I have been called on to apply splints, check tractions, asked about treatments, helped to devise colostomy bags from polythene bags and have occasionally deputised for the matron at the weekend. Some time ago we also did a regular 'night on' call for the whole hospital. Fortunately we were not called out very often, but I do remember being up all one night after having taught all day, then having to teach through until lunchtime the following day.

Whenever I am asked about standards I am pleased to say that our standards compared favourably with Britain. We have staff shortages, lack of basic equipment, and sometimes low morale, but so do the NHS hospitals in the UK. There is always more to do. We do the best we can with the resources that are available. The standard of nurse education is high. I am constantly astonished at the achievements of the students who have had four years secondary education, coming to an institution where in three and a half years they have to gain the knowledge and the ability to function as a general nurse, a midwife or a public health nurse. I congratulate them on their determined effort to succeed and their faith in the God who helps them.

Anne works on a community health scheme in Nepal. While Barbara's work is hospital based, Anne is much closer to our health visitor or district nurse. But the work is no less varied or important. Having trained as a nursery nurse and got married, she worked for two years in India in several creches for children from poor families.

I am now working part time in community health in Pokhara, Nepal. My husband and I are members of the International Nepal Fellowship. The Bazaar Clinic in Pokhara is mainly run by Nepali nurses and the nurse in charge is excellent. She has just the right balance of compassion for the patients and efficiency. Clinics are held there for sick children, antenatal patients, a well baby clinic and there is a very busy morning when vaccinations are given, BCG, polio, tetanus, whooping cough, etc. That morning too we will weigh all the children and fill in their health and weight cards. Then we will give nutrition advice to the mothers of those children who are malnourished. Many of the mothers, even the ones who are better off financially, do not realise that they should be giving their children more than just plain rice to eat.

Thousands of children every year in Nepal die of dehydration due to diarrhoea. They can die in a matter of hours in this way. We teach the mothers to make a rehydration drink for the children, when they fill a glass of water (boiled water if they can afford to boil it) and put in it a teaspoon of sugar and a pinch of salt. Many of the mothers do not know that they should give the children something to drink when they have diarrhoea. They think that drinking fluids will make it worse. One of our neighbours brought her baby to our house one afternoon. The baby, Kanchi, had been vomiting and having attacks of diarrhoea all night and she was lying quite still and limp in her mother's arms. I thought that maybe it was too late to do anything as she was obviously very dehydrated, but I decided that I would try to give her some of the mixture I have just described. I gave it to her in small teaspoonfuls and she drank a large glass and a half of it! What a joy it was to see her almost immediately come back to life and begin to sit up and take notice of what was going on around her.

We also go on home visits to the malnourished children and their families to advise about which foods they should give the children. I always go on home visits with a Nepali nurse and I enjoy going very much. We also give teaching on health and hygiene, family planning and how to make the best use of the land they have and help them to grow as much as possible. Sometimes, we just sit and listen to their problems.

It would be wrong to give the impression that all missionary nurses go abroad long term. There are a diverse number of short-term nursing posts available with a wide variety of agencies. This means a Christian nurse can give of her expertise for a specified period then return to the UK. It is no longer necessary to feel a lifelong vocation to be a missionary. Visa and entry permit restrictions often prevent long-term missionary service in some countries. Most missionary societies and relief agencies have numerous short-term placements on offer and are thrilled to employ Christian nurses in the projects they support in different countries.

Nicola, a midwife who went with TEAR Fund on a short-term assignment to Ethiopia, attempted to help in a desperate emergency.

Stepping on to a plane at London's Heathrow then off again in Addis Ababa, capital of Ethiopia – having never been to the so-called Third World, seemed to be the

culture shock I had been warned about. However, in
the nine months that followed, my standards changed
somewhat. I then looked upon the capital city as the
height of sophistication and plenty when compared to
the more rural areas of southern and northern Ethiopia
where I had been working . . .

The appalling and tragic famine in Ethiopia has affected 90 per cent of the population who strive to live off
their parched, eroded and barren land. I was seconded
by TEAR Fund, together with another British nurse, to
work with SIM-AID, the relief arm of Sudan Interior
Mission. We worked in three areas, and each was completely different.

Our aim was to try to prevent the kind of widespread
disaster which had sadly hit some areas. We wanted to
help people by giving relief aid before life became so
desperate that they had to flee from their villages in a
weakened state in the search for food. Already many
had sold their cattle and goats, indeed anything surplus
such as pots and pans from their kitchens. I met families
who had sold the front door from their mud hut as
firewood in the market in exchange for food. For the
most part, people literally had nothing left. By opening
two feeding centres for very malnourished children to
come to each day, SIM-AID was able to help save many
young lives. The children would arrive by 9 a.m., some
having walked for two or three hours and queue to
receive a bowl of porridge, a cup of high protein milk
(reconstituted with clean water) and a couple of biscuits.
They would have this meal three times a day. Our
Ethiopian colleagues were involved with the day-to-day
running of the feeding centres and preparation of food.

Within four months many children had gained in
strength and weight and were discharged home – but
still more new children came, signifying that their families too had been pushed to the limits of their resources
and could no longer feed them. We wanted to help each
family in the area, so a monthly take-home dry ration

distribution was started. As nurses, our job was to see all the children under five years of age and assess them nutritionally by weighing and measuring them each month – quite a mammoth task. We also began medical clinics, originally for the under-fives, but soon the age limit disappeared and the queues increased. Some we could help – those with dysentery, infections, burns, intestinal parasites, anaemia, vitamin deficiency or malaria. Less fortunate were those who came with TB, chronic arthritis, blindness or gynaecological problems. Sadly we all too often had to say, 'Sorry, no medicine.' The needs were simply vast – the resources few . . .

Often I felt saddened, frustrated and angered by what I saw. There were other countless occasions when I felt joy, satisfaction and encouragement . . . The faith of Ethiopian Christians in such dire circumstances, made a deep, deep impression on me. Not only is there physical famine in Ethiopia but there is also a spiritual one and under the government of that time (1984-1985) it was undoubtedly costly to follow Christ. Yet the Christian Church is alive and well and according to many reports, growing fast.

Other agencies besides relief agencies and missionary societies welcome Christian nurses as recruits for overseas placements. When Voluntary Service Overseas opened its door to nurses, Elizabeth went to Kenya when she was twenty-four.

It was fascinating. Of the twelve nurses who went out to East Africa with me, nine were Christians. We served in mission hospitals. I was attached to a hospital run by the Presbyterian Church of East Africa (PCEA). It was during the unsettled period of the Kikuyu (Mau Mau) troubles, so that added to our problems. We arrived about six weeks after Tom Mboya had been assassinated and within the first week the whole civil war erupted . . . On the first day we were there the pharmacist and his wife were arrested leaving their seven children in hiding with us . . .

Sadly, though I loved the Africans I met, the Christianity of the mission hospital was the 'freeze-dried' variety – dead. It was hard for me to come to the painful realisation that a mission hospital was only as Christian as the staff. The missionaries were not 'alive' – and I was terribly shattered by that because I had not met many nominal Christians before. But then I had the chance to visit another mission hospital upcountry run by the Africa Inland Mission, and there I met people who rejoiced to name the name of Jesus and wanted to sing and praise the Lord. I knew where I was with them. I had felt rather isolated at the hospital where I was working. In the end the factor which kept me going was my visits to Nairobi Baptist Church and the ministry of Tom Houston.

Our work at the hospital carried on despite the troubles and the strikes. My first experience of a strike in hospital was at PCEA. The whole student nurse body walked out. We volunteers were left to run the whole place of ninety beds. So, when I returned to the UK it seemed nothing to be involved in strikes in the NHS after that experience. Nothing could be as bad as having to run a whole hospital . . .

In the end, Elizabeth did not feel God had called her to work as a missionary nurse overseas but she remained in Britain to make a distinguished career within the NHS.

Political regimes appear to come and go at much greater speed than previously. Civil wars erupt with little warning and missionaries sometimes get caught up in these events through no fault of their own – except their desire to care for and serve all in the name of Jesus Christ. Having suffered in this way, many are nevertheless still prepared to return often to the same place and country to continue their missionary service. Two qualities are necessary – courage and stickability in the face of truly tough situations.

One very recent example is the story of Heather Sinclair from Northern Ireland who first offered her services as a nurse and a midwife to TEAR Fund in 1986 believing she was destined to serve in the refugee camps in Thailand. Instead, TEAR Fund asked her if she would be willing to go to southern Sudan to assist in famine relief and mother and baby care in Mundri under the auspices of ACROSS. Four months later, she was captured by the Sudanese People's Liberation Army with her three American colleagues, and taken as a hostage on a long difficult cross-country trek. Seven heart-rending weeks later they were released into the hands of British and American embassy staff on the Kenyan border.

Undeterred by that setback, she went in 1989 to Swaziland and then in 1990 to Thailand as a missionary nurse, to begin a new sphere of service among the Khmer Rouge refugees in the north of the country. Heather's courage and faith in God seemed to take her on – praising Him for His faithfulness – to each new task with joy and a willingness to forget the past and look forward to a new and challenging future.

To conclude this chapter some wise words from Laurence Dopson in his article for the *Nursing Times* about the Nurses' Christian Fellowship are appropriate.

The missionary nurse in the 1990s operates in a changing world. In many developing countries there is no longer a shortage of trained nurses. Hostility to Christianity is reinforced by political and nationalistic attitudes. In the Middle East, fundamentalist Islam frowns on preaching by other religions (though paradoxically there is freedom in Pakistan, another Islamic state). If a native of Nepal alters his or her religion to Christianity, the penalty is a year's imprisonment, and the person who baptises them gets six years and the evangelist three. Political prisoners are not the only prisoners of conscience in today's world, as Amnesty International recognises. Many Governments in the Third World, while only too pleased to accept the assistance of missionary nurses, stipulate no proselytising. Yet in Nepal for instance missionary nurses do not find the limits burdensome. In India Hindu hostility to the Pope's visit exaggerated anti-Christian sentiment, but India, like other countries, restricts nurse missionaries from the West through work permits. Countries which have their own well-trained nurses only want expatriates whose qualifications are in short supply: nurse educationalists and midwives.

In an increasingly secular world, some nurses in this country believe the best way to serve overseas is through governmental agencies. But others still want to obey the biblical direction to go out into the world and preach the gospel.

Missionary nursing is developing. Professionally and pastorally it is now a partnership with the local carers and churches. But clearly there is still a place for the missionary nurse.

16

The Future of Agency and Volunteer Nursing

Dame Audrey Emerton, chairwoman of the United Kingdom Central Council, holds some firm views on how the profession is going to cope with its dire recruitment problems in the 1990s. 'We know because of the drop in the birth rate, "the demographic time bomb", there will be great difficulties in staffing the hospitals properly. This is our main challenge. And the other is – how are we going to maintain the efficiency and effectiveness of our nursing service with an increasingly ageing population?'

In Dame Audrey's opinion, there are two possibilities at least which might help to bridge this yawning gap. 'We see first the new auxiliaries: health care assistants – paid support staff – who will replace students not trained staff and will take on a more prominent role. There will be more and better training for them. Secondly, the NHS is also going to be much more dependent on voluntary help from movements such as the British Red Cross Society and St John Ambulance, etc.'

The importance of Christians being involved in this voluntary band of medical helpers has been proved in Dame Audrey's own case. She has had a lifelong connection with the St John Ambulance from her first experiences as an eleven-year-old cadet in Tunbridge Wells until today, when she has become Commissioner for Kent and Chief

Nursing Officer for the movement for the whole country. She could recall her own early hospital practical experience long before her nursing career started, partly through that movement. Her own summation of the staffing position is: 'I think the whole country generally is going to be more and more dependent on volunteers in the 1990s – partly because we cannot afford the statutory care.'

With the continued shortage of trained staff, many sisters and charge nurses welcome the help and hard work done by different voluntary groups. Each local community close to a hospital should be able to provide voluntary assistance. Sometimes they could be retired people. Obviously some of these groups were intended to help raise desperately needed financial support more than anything else. But, just as important, could be the offers of assistance with art, music, craft-making or gardening, or the wide range of activities that a hospital occupational therapy department or physiotherapy department might include. Today all kinds of skills can be utilised. Usually these helpers are there in the short term, but even then their practical support with, say, driving patients out on home visits, might help rehabilitation from strokes. Drivers are always needed for a variety of roles in most hospitals. The needs are many, and every hospital has great gaps in its stalwart band of volunteers.

Most hospital staffing problems, however, are met by the help of two main groups of paid nursing staff: bank nurses and agency nurses.

In one hospital in London a ward sister puts this use of agency nurses into a different focus, as a problem rather than a benefit, because in her hospital the cost of employing permanent night staff who are agency and bank nurses has led to a cutback in hospital beds overall. So this hospital can no longer afford all these agency nurses, which adds to the ongoing staffing problems. The same sister welcomes the idea of the better-trained health care assistants as under Project 2000, but maintains that it solves nothing when a ward cannot be run by them. They still legally have to have the right ratio of trained to untrained staff on a shift. Out of six staff, three must be trained nurses.

'We also,' she continues, 'have students from the local schools who come in for work experience as part of their careers package. Usually they come for two weeks at a time. They can only do the basics of course, but it is planned by the nurse manager of that unit. They do simple practical tasks such as feeding someone, or reading to them or chatting with a patient.' It seems to be an excellent way for young people to help the local community *and* gain the experience of being on a ward, especially if some are considering becoming nurses.'

Win was one who spoke of the value to her, a late entrant into nursing, of working for a year as a nursing auxiliary at a couple of local hospitals and private homes for elderly patients. That period of work experience helped to confirm to her that God wanted her to become a nurse.

Bank Nursing

Often the staff shortages in Britain's hospitals can be alleviated by the return, part-time, of trained staff who have left to get married and raise a family. However, a lot depends on facilities in hospital for the care of their small children. Many married nurses say they would come back gladly if proper childcare provisions were made. Take the case of Gill, a married nurse with a special qualification in neonatal care, who had an adopted baby to look after. She wanted to do part-time nursing while her husband or her family cared for the baby. Her desire was to do bank nursing in Leicester. The 'bank' is a pool of part-time staff a hospital can call upon when it is short-staffed. Gill usually worked three nights a week in a special neonatal unit that was thirty-two staff short. She was thus attached to the paediatric bank and worked only on that unit. The joy to her was that as a bank nurse she could choose to work when she wanted to. She had not got a contract to work set hours such as ordinary nurses have. If her child was sick or she wanted a week off, she didn't work. It was very like being an agency nurse.

Gill for one, felt the profession did not make it easy for married women to come back into or stay in nursing. She specified the shifts that had to be worked and the lack of facilities to care for the children of married staff. The chief thing she missed as a bank nurse permanently on night duty was the patient contact and the daytime routine of a ward. The night staff missed out also on getting to know the parents of the sick babies who, unless the baby was desperately sick, the staff rarely saw.

Another married nurse, Claire, said she would prefer to do bank nursing if and when she wanted to work fewer hours. Bank nursing was the sensible way to do part-time nursing. She knew already that she did not want to work on night duty and she would choose to be on the bank for a day job. The shortage of nurses meant there would always be part-time nurses' jobs available to her when she chose to pursue them. Like so many other nurses marking time between permanent jobs, Claire had taken an agency nursing post in London. 'I enjoyed it and yet I didn't enjoy it. Usually in bank nursing, however, you are attached to a specific hospital or agency. It was good money but you cannot get close to the patients because you are only there for short spells. Nursing to me is caring for and getting to know my patients and knowing they will be there next morning when I go on duty. I prefer nursing the "whole" person and agency nursing does not seem good for that, especially if you only do a weekly shift of eight hours. Moreover there is no security – you only get paid for the hours you work.'

Agency Nursing

Many nurses find agency nursing a useful way of finding short-term employment or of earning some much needed extra cash. Some NHS staff do agency nursing as well as their regular job in order to earn extra money. This is known as 'moonlighting' and definitely is *not* approved of as doing two jobs reduces a nurse's energy.

Sometimes the short-term agency nursing post becomes long term. Having been abroad, Staff Nurse Heather decided to take a post advertised with a nursing agency at the Norwich and Norfolk Hospital with the British Nursing Association (BNA). It was a long-term post in fact and it gave her time to take stock and pray about what God intended her to do next. She stayed seven months before moving on to do an Oncology course in London.

Other examples of part-time nursing jobs were not happy. Jackie had done a great deal of agency nursing. At one stage she worked for the agency itself allocating nurses their jobs. Her own view was that although she might earn more as an agency nurse her hours were not as long or as secure. 'You were paid by the hour. You might be booked in for an eight-hour shift but if, after four, they discovered they had enough nurses, they sent the agency nurses home.' She worked for four years as an agency nurse. She admitted she learnt a lot but looking back on it she had not enjoyed the experience. The agency asked each new applicant all kinds of questions such as, 'Can you do intensive care?' 'Can you do geriatrics?' Jackie just said 'Yes' to them all. As a result her work did at least have a certain measure of variety!

The disadvantage of agency nursing is that it does not allow the nurse to build up relationships long term with the patients. The advantage for a married woman with a family is flexibility. 'I found it easier not to be committed to a ward and the responsibility of running it,' said Jackie. 'There is no sense of letting anyone down. I personally believe you only do agency nursing for the money and the hours which fit in with the task of looking after a husband and children.'

17

Christianity in Hospital

'I believe the Church has a definite function in nurturing and supporting people who are at the coal face of interaction with human need.'

Baroness Jean McFarlane of Llandaff

The names of many of Britain's oldest hospitals – St Bartholomew's, St Thomas's, St Joseph's – make it clear that they were originally Christian foundations. The same cannot be said of the more modern medical establishments, yet each hospital should offer patients some form of religious or spiritual care.

Since the introduction of the Nursing Process with its emphasis on assessing the needs of the whole individual, the spiritual needs of patients should be considered as important as their physical, emotional and psychological needs. Are Christian nurses more able to help patients at this level? There are many intimate moments on the ward when only the nurse is present – and some spiritual need is apparent. Some nurses speak of patients expressing their terror as they face a major operation – the fear that they will not survive – and there are Christian nurses who are able, then and there to reassure them and pray with them. Others tell their patients that they will also pray for them at home and in church. The ministry is ongoing and does not end when the nurse goes off duty. There are also occasions when a nurse, known to her colleagues as a committed Christian, has been asked by other nurses to give a patient spiritual help.

Barbara Simsen, an Australian nurse and midwife tutor, has made spiritual care in hospitals her special study. She claims that it is more than 'religious' care or the chaplain's care. But it took her a very long time to recognise how she herself should offer spiritual care. After years of uncertainty she began to feel free as a nurse to offer spiritual care and to do it for the right motive. 'Then it was because of my understanding and awareness of the patient's need more than my need that I gave it, not as previously, because of my evangelical desire to witness or do something "spiritual". I realised that this was what caused me unrest for years and was the source of my conflict as a Christian nurse.' To encourage her, after she had made that discovery, there were many times when a patient's need of spiritual care became obvious and spurred her on to be able to minister, sometimes with prayer or conversation or with a Bible verse.

However, in the Britain of the 1990s when Christianity is no longer the ethos behind the National Health hospitals and the population is multiracial and multicultural, there is a dilemma. Barbara has pondered and worked through this for herself when doing some of her research here. What was a Christian way of approaching someone of another faith, and what could be considered compromise? She discovered that the way forward might lie in being much more ready to learn from patients of other cultures and other faiths, to learn to understand their perspective. 'Then in being willing to do that, I earn the right to share my Christian perspective. In the past, I have been afraid that I might be contaminated if I dared really listen to a Muslim, for instance. But when I talked to a devout Muslim lady recently I learned a great deal from her and could talk about my beliefs to her.'

Another new perspective was that of the Roman Catholic. During a speaking itinerary she had visited Roman Catholic convents and hospitals to give workshops on spiritual care. She had felt very alone in one hospital but, as she left the chapel, the nuns who had been at her workshop made her welcome and invited her for coffee and they were soon sharing their own experiences of spiritual care. Whatever her inhibitions, what became important then was not what divided them but what commonality there was between them. 'I learnt something very profound on that occasion.'

In an article published in the *Nursing Times*, Barbara wrote challengingly, 'There is little consideration in our nursing education of spiritual issues. Where it does appear it is centred on religious practices, especially those surrounding birth and death. This preoccupation has done us a severe disservice. At the very least it has caused us to miss the point of spirituality. Arranging for the last rites to be performed before it is too late (but not too early lest it frighten the patient), offering to arrange for a clergy visit, or ordering a special diet, have become tasks to be done, often seen as optional extras, rather than an integral means of achieving important goals of care.' And again, 'Hope must be seen by the carers as something more than that which is invested only in prolonged mortality (a cure) – or immortality.'

The work of chaplains

There appears to be a marked degree of difference between one hospital and the next as to the visibility and availability of the chapel and the chaplain. Some chaplains are unwilling to take time to sit and listen, as well as talk to, patients about their deepest fears. They are willing to visit the patient briefly and bring them the sacrament but do not want to stay and become involved personally with them and have little spiritual life to offer. Others are wonderful at being prepared to spend time with the patients and to help Christian nurses break perhaps deeply distressing news to them about their condition. They are happy to be alongside the patients at their lowest and most unspiritual ebb, sharing their happy moments as well as their angry ones. They are able to pray with a patient and minister to them.

If the hospital is a Christian place of healing, such as the Mildmay Hospice or St Christopher's Hospice, then the chaplains have a much more clear-cut and upfront role and become a major part of the hospice management team. Usually, too, those appointed are ordained men or women who possess the deep humanity and spirituality which enables them to be a strength and comfort to somebody who is facing death. Their concern is not to convert the dying patient – though that would be a wonderful event if it happened – but, as Dr Cicely Saunders expressed it: 'No one can think of imposing their own faith upon another person, least of all when they are helpless, but those who have a belief that there is love, meaning and purpose hidden in these mysteries see many of their patients finding relief and peace in their own way.' (*Cicely Saunders* by Shirley du Boulay, Hodder & Stoughton)

Christian doctors and nurses play a crucial role in any medical mission in the UK too.

Support groups

Alongside the work of nurses and chaplains, supporting the spiritual and loving care they offer to patients, there are various groups of Christians who have been linked by their religious faith in various fellowships or guilds. In different hospitals these may take on different names – some are affiliated to groups such as the Nurses' Christian Fellowship, the Hospital Christian Fellowship, the Guild of Catholic Nurses or Caring Professions Concern.

Another element of importance in hospital life can be the hospital radio and that usually makes use of various groups represented within the staff. On Sundays in some hospitals it is the Christian Union which produces and broadcasts a brief fifteen minute service to the wards. Some nurses have linked up to the Christian Hospital Radio group and received helpful training and advice on making scripts for broadcasting and technical know-how.

Over the past twenty years or so the nominalism of much of church life has given way to a more lively and spirit-filled worship, and there are more growing Christian churches where spiritual teaching is building up the congregation in spirit and in truth. Today most nurses can get to church at least once on a Sunday. This was not so when the NCF came into being some fifty years ago. At that time the Christian nurse had rare opportunities to attend a church and the NCF's weekly meeting in the nurses' home began and prospered, almost as a substitute for church. There were tremendous blessings and nurses were converted and many grew in spiritual maturity within the ranks of the organisation.

In the past these Fellowship meetings were not attended by doctors or other paramedical staff – some indeed had their own Christian Fellowships. It is a sign of happier days that today most Hospital Fellowships are usually attended by Christians from all the medical disciplines. The Christian Medical Fellowship for doctors does still hold separate meetings, but have recently organised joint CMF/NCF events for the first time. The Guild of Catholic Doctors too is active in many hospitals.

Baroness Jean McFarlane of Llandaff had learnt the hard way in her varied professional career that her Christianity, her church life and her professional life seemed to be in totally separate compartments. However, once in Manchester while teaching nurses and finding a supportive church locally, this was no longer true. There she was able to push through and implement her Nursing Process care plan and watch the profession take it up and use it. She felt that she had witnessed a revolution in standards of care in her own lifetime as a Christian nurse – and against an increasingly secular mood in society. Thus, too, the whole value system underlying nursing had increasingly impressed her as important as she developed and put into practice in her teaching programme a course on values and ethics in nursing.

Over recent years, it has been her joy to see how her faith and her practice have become one. She has wise words of counsel to churches seeking to support their members working in hospitals. At her own church, for example, she has been seeking to encourage a ministry of health and healing with a commissioning service for Christian doctors and nurses. 'I believe the Church has a definite function in nurturing and supporting people who are at the coal face of interaction with human need.'

The challenge remains. As John Stott stated it: 'Too often Christianity influences the world as much as a mouse influences a cat – it is swallowed up by it.' Christian nurses need to find that Christlike distinctiveness that will not be swallowed up by the world yet will bridge the gap between them and the Samaritan woman, the fallen and the healthy, the grieving and the rejoicing. This is the path the Master walked and Christian nurses have to tread it daily as they seek to bring holistic care to a fallen world.

Resource List of Useful Sources
of Information

PUBLICATIONS

Aids: A Christian Response by Roy McCloughry and Carol Bebawi. Grove Booklet No.64 Ethical Studies, Grove Books Ltd, Bramcote, Nottingham NG9 3DS.

Aids: A Strategy for Nursing Care by Robert Pratt. Edward Arnold Ltd.

Beyond Healing by Jennifer Rees Larcombe. Hodder Christian Paperback.

Careers in Nursing and Allied Professions by R. Clark. Kogan Page Ltd.

Cicely Saunders: The founder of the modern hospice movement by Shirley du Boulay. Hodder & Stoughton.

Dream or Nightmare? The Closure of Longstay Mental Hospitals and Community Care – Report of the Quaker Social Responsibility & Education group. Friends House, Euston Road, London NW1.

Heaven Can Wait by Max Sinclair. Hodder Christian Paperback.

HMSO leaflets and publicity materials about careers in nursing.

He Sent Them Out by Dr Andrew Fergusson. The Story of the Bermondsey and Brook Lane Medical Mission.

Issues Facing Christians Today by John R. W. Scott. Marshalls.

Nurses Notes to God by Marion Wilcox RN. Herald Press, Scottdale, Pennsylvania, Kitchener, Ontario.

No Bronze Statue – the story of the Mildmay Mission Hospital by Phyllis Thompson. Kingsway Publishers.

Nursing Times & Nursing Mirror, 4 Little Essex Street, London WC2 3LF.

Only One Way Up by Kristine Gibbs. Darton Longman & Todd.

Pacemaker, Quarterly journal of the Nurses' Christian Fellowship.

Poems by Nurses published by the NCF, Bawtry Hall, South Parade, Bawtry, Doncaster DN10 6JH.

Spiritual Needs and Resources in Illness and Hospitalisation unpublished thesis by Barbara Simsen. Available from 4 Gaddum Road, Didsbury, Manchester M20 0SZ.

ORGANISATIONS

This list is not exhaustive but refers to organisations many of which are mentioned in the text of the book.

AFRICA INLAND MISSION, 2 Vorley Road, London N19 5HE.

AIDS CARE EDUCATION TRAINING, PO Box 1323, London W5 5TF.

BAPTIST UNION HEALTH AND HEALING FELLOWSHIP, The Manse, Western Road, Hawkhurst, Kent TN18 4BT.

BERMONDSEY & BROOK LANE MEDICAL MISSION, 5 Oaklands Road, Bromley, Kent BR1 3SJ.

BRITISH NURSING ASSOCIATION 3rd Floor, 443 Oxford Street, London W1R.

CAFOD, (Catholic) 2 Garden Close, Stockwell Road, London SW9 9TY.

CARING PROFESSIONS CONCERN, 34a Hilltop Road, Earley, Reading, Berks RG6 1DB.

CATHOLIC GUILD OF DOCTORS, 20 Long Oaks Court, Sketty, Swansea, Glam SA2 OQX.

CATHOLIC NURSES GUILD, 4 Five Acres, Wilford, Notts NG11 7FP.

CARE (Christian Action Research and Education), 53 Romney Street, London SW1P 3RF.

CHRISTIAN AID, PO Box 100, London SE1 7RT.

CHRISTIAN CONCERN FOR THE MENTALLY HANDICAPPED, 118B Oxford Road, Reading, Berks RG1 7NG.

CHRISTIAN HOSPITAL RADIO FELLOWSHIP, PO Box 11, Tunbridge Wells, Kent TN2 3NE.

CHRISTIAN IMPACT, Institute for Contemporary Christianity, St Peter's Church, Vere Street, London W1M 9PH.

CHRISTIAN MEDICAL FELLOWSHIP, 157 Waterloo Road, London SE1 8XN.

CHURCH MISSIONARY SOCIETY, 157 Waterloo Road, London SE1 8UU.

CHURCH OF ENGLAND BOARD FOR SOCIAL RE-SPONSIBILITY, Church House, Dean's Yard, Westminster, London SW1P 3NZ.

CHURCH OF SCOTLAND BOARD FOR SOCIAL RE-SPONSIBILITY, 121 George Street, Edinburgh EH2 4YN.

CHURCH OF SCOTLAND BOARD FOR WORLD MISSION, 121 George Street, Edinburgh EH2 4YN.

DEPARTMENT OF HEALTH, Central Office of Information, Hercules Road, London SE1.

EDINBURGH MEDICAL MISSIONARY SOCIETY, 14 Mayfield Terrace, Edinburgh EH9 1SA.

EVANGELICAL MISSIONARY ALLIANCE, 186 Kennington Park Road, London SE11 4BT.

FREE CHURCH FEDERAL COUNCIL, Hospital Chaplaincy Board, 27 Tavistock Square, London WC1H 9HH.

HER MAJESTY'S STATIONERY OFFICE, 49 High Holborn, London WC1.

HOSPITAL CHAPLAINCIES COUNCIL, General Synod of the Church of England, Church House, Great Smith Street, London SW1P 3NZ.

INTERNATIONAL NEPAL FELLOWSHIP, 2 West Street, Reading, Berks RG1 1TT.

INTERNATIONAL HOSPITAL CHRISTIAN FELLOWSHIP, Baron van Nagellstraat 9, 3781 APVOORTHUIZEN Holland.

JOINT COMMITTEE FOR HOSPITAL CHAPLAINCY, (RC/Anglican/Free Church) 27 Tavistock Square, London WC1H 9HH.

L'ARCHE, 14 London Road, Beccles, Suffolk NR34 9NH.

THE LEPROSY MISSION INTERNATIONAL, 50 Windmill Road, Brentford, Middx TW8 OQA.

LUDHIANA BRITISH FELLOWSHIP, 157 Waterloo Road, London SE1 8UU.

MENTAL HEALTH FOUNDATION, 8 Hallam Street, London W1N 6DH.

MEDICAL MISSIONARY ASSOCIATION, 244 Camden Road, London NW1 9HE.

METHODIST CHURCH BOARD FOR SOCIAL RESPONSIBILITY, 1 Central Buildings, Westminster, London SW1H 9NH.

METHODIST CHURCH OVERSEAS DIVISION, 25 Marylebone Road, London NW1 5JR.

MINISTRY OF HEALING COMMITTEE, United Reformed Church, 86 Tavistock Square, London WC1H 9RT.

MILDMAY MISSION HOSPITAL AND TRAINING CENTRE, Hackney Road, Shoreditch, London E2 7NA.

THE NATIONAL BOARDS:

ENGLISH NATIONAL BOARD FOR NURSING, MIDWIFERY AND HEALTH VISITING Career Information Section, PO Box 356, Sheffield S8 OSJ.

For Nurse training:
Nurses Central Clearing House, PO Box 346, Bristol BS99 7FB.
WALES – The Chief Nursing Officer, Welsh Office, Cathays Park, Cardiff CF1 3NQ.
For Nurse Training:
Welsh National Board, 13th Floor Pearl Assurance House, Greyfriars Road, Cardiff CF1 3AG.
SCOTLAND – The Nursing Adviser, Scottish Health Service Centre, Crewe Road South, Edinburgh EH4 2LF.
NORTHERN IRELAND – The Recruitment Officer, National Board of Nursing, Northern Ireland, RAC House, 79 Chichester Street, Belfast BT1 4JR.

NATIONAL SCHIZOPHRENIA FELLOWSHIP, 68 Testwood Road, Windsor, Berks SL4 5RP.
NURSES' CHRISTIAN FELLOWSHIP, Bawtry Hall, South Parade, Bawtry, Doncaster DN10 6JL.
NURSES' CHRISTIAN FELLOWSHIP INTERNATIONAL, PO Box 224, Warrington WA5 5EW.
OVERSEAS MISSIONARY FELLOWSHIP, Belmont, The Vine, Sevenoaks, Kent TN13 3TZ.
PILGRIM HOMES, 175 Tower Bridge Road, London SE1 2AL.
ROYAL COLLEGE OF MIDWIVES, 15 Mansfield Street, London W1M 0BE.
ROYAL COLLEGE OF NURSING, 20 Cavendish Square, London W1.
THE SALVATION ARMY, Social and Medical Work, 101 Queen Victoria Street, London EC4P 4EP.
THE SHAFTESBURY PROJECT, 79 Maid Marian Way, Nottingham NG1 6AE.
THE SHAFTESBURY SOCIETY, 2a Amity Grove, Raynes Park, London SE20 0LJ.
SUDAN INTERIOR MISSION INTERNATIONAL, Joint Mission Centre, Ullswater Crescent, Coulsdon, Surrey CR3 2HR.

TEAR FUND, 100 Station Road, Teddington, Middx TW11 8QE.

UNITED KINGDOM CENTRAL COUNCIL FOR NURSING, MIDWIFERY AND HEALTH VISITING, 23 Portland Place, London W1N 3AF.

VOLUNTARY SERVICES OVERSEAS LTD, 317 Putney Bridge Road, London SW15.